The
Business
of
Learning
to
Relax

by

Celia M. Bibby

B.A.(Hons) Psy. M.Sc.(Eng.) CHP. MTAE (Ret'd)

Stress Management for
The New Millennium

FIRST EDITION

Published by Bibby Publishing Limited
Publisher David M. Bibby
Text Design & Composition: Sioux Peto (LB Graphics)
Graphics: Sioux Peto (LB Graphics), Cliff Dellar (Delgraphics)
Original Audio Recording and Mastering: Barn Room Studios, Kingsdown
Cover Picture, Picture of Business Woman and Woman in Gym
by Melvin Silcock Photography

International Standard Book Number: 9-780953-635009

Printed by JEM Digital Print Services Ltd, Sittingbourne, Kent

Authored and Edited by
Celia M. Bibby, BA(Hons), Psy. M.Sc (Eng.) CHP MTAE (Ret'd)

PREFACE

Dear Reader let me introduce myself. My name is Celia Bibby and I have worked as a Management Consultant advising City companies how they can keep their business executives healthy, stress-free and therefore more efficient and productive.

I am also a psychologist who has made a particular study of the effects of stress on individuals in the working environment and how this can be best ameliorated using the body's own natural resources. Over the next ten weeks I would like us to work together to explore various ways in which we can all help ourselves to become fitter and less stressed and therefore more able to withstand the pressures of working in a hectic city environment.

To celebrate the twenty second anniversary of the introduction of City Relaxation Consultancy to the workplace, I am pleased to be able to offer to those who have not had the opportunity to attend one of my courses, the means of learning how to relax through this book and the accompanying audio.

As you have already taken the commitment of buying this book with its accompanying audio you have shown that you too have an interest and need to learn how to relax and benefit from the process of deep relaxation technique and I am delighted to have the opportunity of helping you to achieve this.

Celia M. Bibby

CONTENTS

CHAPTER X

RELAXATION SESSION

INTRODUCTION

This book has been written in the form of 10 Chapters. Chapters I and II should be read first but the remaining chapters can be read in the order in which the reader finds most relevant.

After each chapter the accompanying audio should be played (this takes about 20 minutes). There are instructions and suggestions at the end of each chapter to assist the reader in getting the most out of the relaxation session, as well as useful tips and addresses of organisations offering additional advice.

This book is designed to reproduce the benefits of a ten-week course in relaxation to be taken at the reader's convenience. No special equipment is required, other than a quiet room or space, a comfortable chair or rug on the floor and a player for the accompanying audio. Ideally each chapter should be read a week apart with the relaxation session being practised during the week. This will allow time for the brain to assimilate the information given and for the body to adjust if a lifestyle change is being made, ie: stopping smoking.

This course has been designed for business executives but the principles apply to anyone whose life is becoming stressed.

The audio can be played quite safely to all but it is advisable that you make sure that you are quite wide awake at the end of each track before driving a car or operating machinery. A cup of tea or coffee or a short walk is suggested.

CHAPTER I

In this first chapter I am going to explain to you, with the aid of diagrams, the basic principles underlying the problem of stress and its effect on our physiology and how the technique of deep relaxation can reverse or minimise these effects. I have four objectives, which I hope we will achieve over the next ten weeks and these objectives have been set out below as a permanent reminder of what this course sets out to achieve for you.

OBJECTIVES

1. To provide an awareness of stress, primarily in yourself, but also in others. This is especially important for people in supervisory roles.

2. Identify specific stress related areas in your working, social and personal life and provide coping techniques.

3. Replacement of negative health patterns with positive health patterns. Example: Stopping smoking and taking more exercise.

4. Practice of relaxation technique to prevent tension building to a point where it starts to affect our health.

The Business of Learning to Relax

Many people say that they know what stress is but are unclear to what it really means in relation to our bodily response. To clarify matters you will see set below 4 questions and answers relating to stress.

Let us go through these in turn.

Q. *What is stress?*

A. Scientists define stress as "a pressure or stimulus which cannot be tolerated."

Q. *Why is it harmful?*

A. The body uses the "general adaptation syndrome", to react to stress, as a defensive mechanism. It circulates adrenaline and steroid hormones to enable the body to flee from impending danger.

This reaction, however, is geared to physical stress rather than modern day psychological stress and the result is that the adrenaline and steroids build up in the body instead of being utilised for flight. Irritability, frustration, bad temper and fatigue follow from this.

Q. *What can be done to help the modern day business man or woman who is under stress but who leads a sedentary lifestyle?*

A. Teach him or her to become aware of the build up of tension in the body and how to reduce this to a safe level for that individual by practising the relaxation technique taught in this course.

He or she should also be encouraged to develop a positive attitude regarding diet and exercise and to be fully aware of the dangers associated with cigarette smoking, dependence on tranquillisers and other potentially addictive drugs, and the problems of over-indulgence in alcohol.

Q. *Why should I use this Relaxation Technique as opposed to other stress relieving methods?*

A. The technique taught in this book and the audio uses the body's natural resources, no medication is required and therefore there is no danger of side effects. This relaxation technique has been proven to be effective in reducing blood pressure and relieving heart strain.

Let me now return to the General Adaption Syndrome, which is the body's reaction to danger and expand a little on this.

We, that is homo-sapiens, are just one step higher on the evolutionary scale than the animals and we still share with them many of the characteristics of survival. For example, we have the primal reaction to fear - gooseflesh - in the animal and bird kingdom this is shown as stiffened fur or feathers to make the animal or bird look larger or more formidable to its enemies.

The butterflies in the stomach feeling which we have all felt on occasions is the same reaction which prevents an animal stopping to eat in the face of danger - similarly with upset bowels - this in the animal species is to allow the animal to run faster - it gives a weight advantage.

Ethnologists, scientists who study the facial expressions of different races, have pointed to the similarity between the facial expressions of man and many of the lower species, particularly those which relate to mating, defence of territory, and fear. For example when we are under stress our muscles tense and tighten, our face muscles force our nose and throat wide open, saliva production decreases and our pupils dilate. All these reactions are life saving in the presence of physical danger - for example running at full pelt across a field to flee the mad fury of a charging bull, when the extra adrenalin released by the adrenal glands enables us to clear the six foot gate, a feat we would never be able to accomplish in the normal relaxed state. *See page 6.*

Fortunately, we are luckier than our ancestors in that we are rarely called upon if ever to hunt for our food, wrestle with wild animals, or perform feats of great athletic courage. Life, apart from the threat of nuclear war, is a great deal safer for the industrialised man and woman than it was in the distant past. However it is a paradox of the 20th century that, although life expectancy in children and young people has improved enormously, the life expectancy of middle-aged people over the last 100 years is threatened by heart disease and cancer of the lung which are the most common causes of death in this age group within the industrialised nations. Stress-related illnesses and complaints now account for between 50-75% of visits to the doctor.

On the following page you will see there is a fairly lengthy list of everyday symptoms which the majority of people could experience at sometime in their lives. Perhaps you could just place a tick against any of those, which you are familiar with. You aren't expected to tick all the items but I should expect that at least one item will be ticked. Everybody must have experienced a headache at sometime!

I will now go on to illustrate with the aid of diagrams the relationship between the symptoms we all experience and our body's response. On *page 7* there is a diagram *Fig 1*, which shows the stress points of the human body with the associated symptoms.

As you will note there is no part of the human organism, which is not affected in some degree or other by stress.

If we are going to try to counteract the effects of stress on our bodies it is important that we understand in simple terms the way in which the major organs function, and since it is the cardiovascular system which is the chief target area of the businessman or woman's stress we will be looking at the function of the heart and lungs. These are illustrated in a very simple fashion in *Fig 2* and *Fig 3* on *pages 8 and 11*.

The two major problems of the heart in the adult are coronary heart disease and hypertension e.g. high blood pressure. If you look at *Fig 2 page* 8 you will see that, since the body's pumping mechanism, the heart, and the piping network of arteries and veins are all one system, it is understandable that any defect in one part of the system will have its effect on the other. Therefore coronary heart disease and hypertension are often experienced together.

The heart as a piece of machinery is a very efficient mechanism. It is a pump which lasts for over 70 years, which pumps more than $2\frac{1}{2}$ million times - and circulates between 40 and 80 million gallons of essential fuel. There must be many engineers who would be pleased to have a man-made pump, which worked so well for so long!

MY PERSONAL CHECK LIST OF STRESS SYMPTOMS

Headache *(mild)* . . . .

Migraine . . . .

Dry mouth . . . .

Pins and Needles in hands or feet . .

Irritability . . . .

Morning tiredness . . . .

Early morning waking *(4am)* . . . . . .

Tremor Indigestion . . . .

Irritable colon *(bowel movements)* . . . .

Low libido *(reduced sex drive)* . . . .

Hot and cold sweats Palpitations . . .

Pain and tightness in the chest
(always seek medical advice)

Skin rash . . . .

Over-eating . . . .

Loss of appetite . . . .

Increase in smoking or drinking . . .

Accident proneness . . . .

Muscle tension . . . .
(particularly in lower back)

ADRENALINE IN ACTION

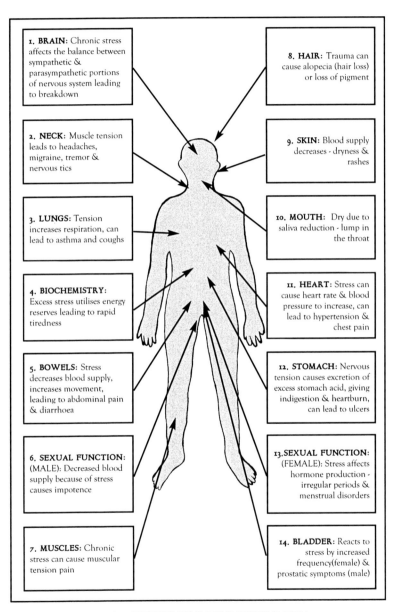

1. BRAIN: Chronic stress affects the balance between sympathetic & parasympathetic portions of nervous system leading to breakdown

2. NECK: Muscle tension leads to headaches, migraine, tremor & nervous tics

3. LUNGS: Tension increases respiration, can lead to asthma and coughs

4. BIOCHEMISTRY: Excess stress utilises energy reserves leading to rapid tiredness

5. BOWELS: Stress decreases blood supply, increases movement, leading to abdominal pain & diarrhoea

6. SEXUAL FUNCTION: (MALE): Decreased blood supply because of stress causes impotence

7. MUSCLES: Chronic stress can cause muscular tension pain

8. HAIR: Trauma can cause alopecia (hair loss) or loss of pigment

9. SKIN: Blood supply decreases - dryness & rashes

10. MOUTH: Dry due to saliva reduction - lump in the throat

11. HEART: Stress can cause heart rate & blood pressure to increase, can lead to hypertension & chest pain

12. STOMACH: Nervous tension causes excretion of excess stomach acid, giving indigestion & heartburn, can lead to ulcers

13. SEXUAL FUNCTION: (FEMALE): Stress affects hormone production - irregular periods & menstrual disorders

14. BLADDER: Reacts to stress by increased frequency(female) & prostatic symptoms (male)

Fig. 1. - STRESS POINTS IN THE BODY

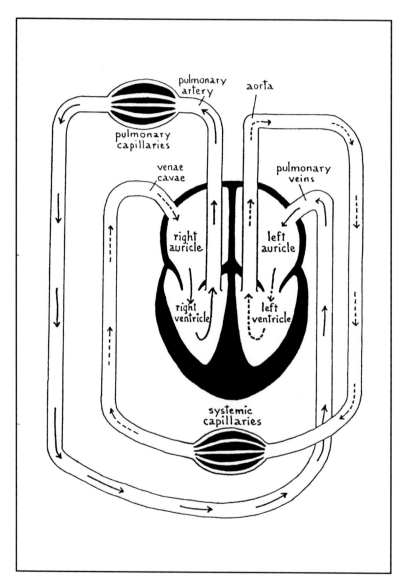

Fig. 2. - THE BLOOD VASCULAR SYSTEM

FACTORS IN HEART DISEASE

1. *A family history of heart disease*
2. *Diabetes mellitus*
3. *Certain factors of personality characterised by aggression and "mental toughness"*
4. *Raised blood cholesterol and blood lipids*
5. *Hypertension*
6. *The Pill in women over 35*
7. *Tobacco smoking*
8. *Obesity*
9. *Lack of physical exercise*

In this chapter we have covered briefly factors Nos. 1 and 5 and we shall be covering the other factors in the remaining chapters.

FACTS ON HYPERTENSION

1. *Normal blood pressure lies between 120/80 and 140/90 for an adult with higher rates for babies, small children and elderly people.*
2. *A borderline case is between 140-159 systolic or between 90-94 diastolic.*
3. *High blood pressure is that greater than 159 systolic or 94 diastolic.*
4. *There are two types of hypertension. Essential hypertension and hypertension associated with the malfunction of another organ such as the kidneys.*
5. *Essential hypertension can be hereditary, it can be due to ageing or obesity.*
6. *Research is still continuing on the link between excess cholesterol in the diet and hypertension.*
7. *Systolic pressure is the measure of pressure in the artery. A cuff containing a closed bladder is inflated increasing pressure to very high levels and ultimately collapsing the underlying artery. A stethoscope is placed over the artery to listen for sounds. Gradually air is let out of the bladder. When the pressure in the bladder falls below the pressure in the artery, a squirt of blood will come through the artery. This motion of blood set in action creates a sound and this first sound is recorded as the highest component of blood pressure. The sounds continue as long as the artery is constricted by the cuff.*
8. *Diastolic pressure is the pressure at which the turbulent sounds disappear when the cuff no longer restricts the artery.*

When you are actively exercising or emotionally upset it is higher than when you are resting quietly or sleeping. But when it is elevated above what is considered normal for most of the day you are considered to have high blood pressure.

Research is still continuing as to other factors which could contribute such as an excess of cholesterol in the diet, but anthropological studies have shown that there is a link between high blood pressure and city life and also that frequent changes of residence from one area to another and even promotion are positively correlated.

The effect of high blood pressure on the heart is that it causes it to work harder and it thereby enlarges.

I want you to now think about the main function of the heart, which is to supply, through the circulation of the blood, all the tissues in the body with the necessary oxygen for the body's cells to survive. This oxygen comes from the air we breathe into our lungs and the more correctly we breathe, the more efficiently our bodies will be able to utilise the oxygen received.

You may think - well everyone knows how to breathe - it comes naturally - yes, that is true, provided you are calm and relaxed and remember to sit and walk with good posture, but in real life we often forget about sitting and walking correctly and we also get tense and harassed and our breathing suffers in turn.

If you could now look at the illustration of the lungs on *Fig.3 page 11* , you will see that the diaphragm, which is situated just below the lungs, moves downward with every intake of air to allow the lungs to expand and then moves upwards when the lungs contract with the outward breath. The ribs move sideways to allow for this movement.

It is not the amount of air that is important when breathing but rather the depth of air breathed in. A calm and relaxed person will breathe low down in the body whereas the tense and anxious person will breathe rapidly, high in the chest. This can lead to the condition known as hyperventilation when rapid overbreathing leads to the balance of carbon dioxide in the blood being disturbed and dizziness occurs. The best cure for this condition is to ask the person so afflicted to breathe deeply and slowly into a paper bag held over their nose and mouth, which will restore the carbon dioxide balance again.

BREATHING TECHNIQUE

Since correct breathing is vital to the practice of Deep Relaxation Technique I think it is now time to see how successful you can be at breathing correctly.

Can you therefore please settle down comfortably in your chair, loosen anything which is restrictive around your chest and waist, put your hands gently in your lap and breathe in very gently through your nose and then out again slowly and gently. Repeat this twice more.

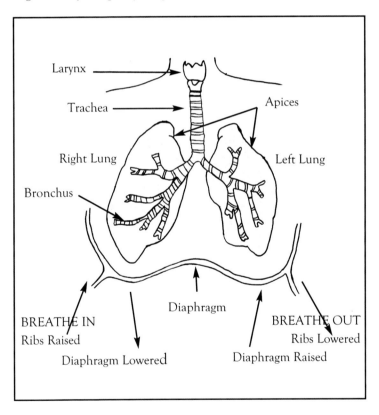

Fig. 3. - THE RESPIRATORY SYSTEM

Now I would like you to place your hands lightly on your abdomen and, as you breathe in again gently, this time I want you to feel your abdomen rise slightly under your hands. Breathe out again, equally gently, taking just a fraction longer over it than you did breathing in, and feel your abdomen drop back again. Repeat this exercise again in your own time and pace when you are ready.

Unless you have a cold, try to breathe in and out through your nose. Try to have as little movement on your upper chest as possible. The reason for trying to exhale slightly longer than you inhale is because breathing in involves muscle contraction and the heart and metabolism speed up slightly; breathing out involves relaxation and the heart and metabolism slow down. This exercise can be practised for two or three minute's several times a day. It may seem strange at first but with practice it will become perfectly natural.

Always try to sit up as well supported in a chair as you possibly can, as the lungs cannot expand properly if your body is hunched over, the same applies when standing and walking, keep the back straight as possible and the shoulders down and back so that the lungs are working with the other muscles in the body and not against them. If you are a smoker you may find some of the breathing exercises difficult or even painful, if so, just do them as well as you can without strain, and I will be discussing the problems of smoking in Chapter III.

PREPARING FOR RELAXATION

Before you begin the relaxation session using the audio, which comes with this book, I would like to give you a few tips to help you to get the maximum benefit from the session.

Firstly you should arrange your relaxation session to take place in a place where you can guarantee you will not be disturbed for at least 30 minutes. If necessary put a DO NOT DISTURB notice on the door, and take the telephone off the hook or switch on the answering machine.

Make sure you have a comfortable place to lie down, with rug or pillow to support your head and a player for the audio.

LEARNING TO VISUALISE

At first, when you listen to the audio, you will be concentrating on my voice and what I am saying to you, but as you begin to feel more and more relaxed you can allow your mind to wander and let relaxing images and thoughts enter in. You may have of course your own mind pictures which help you to relax, but if you have trouble imagining relaxing images and sounds, I have included at the end of every chapter a visualisation suggestion which you can use and which will help you to relax even more and obtain the most pleasure from the session.

Now that you have learnt to breathe deeply and fully I think this is the time for us to start the relaxation technique.

If you have followed the instructions given previously regarding privacy I would like you to remove your shoes and put them out of the way underneath your chair.

If you are likely to be distracted by excess light pull the curtains or adjust the window blinds. Some people find a soft light (40 watts) is better than total darkness.

When you are ready can you take a rug and, using it to lay on or as a pillow for your head, neck or lower back, please lie down on the floor. If you find it painful or difficult to lay down, remain in your chair.

Once you have arranged a comfortable position for yourself, read the Visualisation page TWICE, and put on the Audio Track 2. The relaxation session will last approximately 20 minutes so allow yourself this time in which you know you will be undisturbed. It will not harm you if you are interrupted during a session but the benefits of the session will be lost.

NOW READ THE VISUALISATION PAGE

PLAY THE AUDIO

AND

FOLLOW THE RELAXATION TECHNIQUE

VISUALISATION NO. 1 - CLOUDS

Think about all the types of clouds there are; large white cumulus clouds, heaped upon one
another like cottonwool balls high on a plate,

Or the hair like cirrus with its tendrils of white vapour trailing cross the sky,

Or the rain bearing nimbus grey and heavy ready to pour down upon the earth,

And finally the horizontal spread of the stratus clouds at its best when seen against the
setting sun.

Mounds of water vapour drawn into such a variety of shapes, forever changing, the effects
of colour on those shapes, sometimes lit like lanterns from below by the angle of sun,
sometimes letting through a shaft of golden light which pierces it forming a natural
stairway from the earth through to the sky above.

Light fluffy clouds suspended in a sea of blue on a summer's day. interspersed with the
vapour trails of aircraft now long gone.

Morning clouds vaporising in the midday sun, reforming in the afternoon and bringing
shade.

Evening clouds watching the day sink away below the horizon, and night clouds drifting
silently across the face of the moon.

They move effortlessly without man's help, yet if we try to enter them they dissolve into
water droplets around us, like hillside mist.

They exist, yet they constantly defy boundaries, at their best they are seen through our
eyes when the brain can project its own special significance to each form, like children
who see animals, castles, and fairy forms among the red, gold, purple and white candy
floss that floats above them.

Think then of clouds, moving fast, or gently drifting, bright or dark,
heavy or light.

Imagine that you too are as the clouds, perfectly free to wander wherever you will,
looking down at the world below, seeing it yet no longer part of it, the world and its
problems are down there but you have transcended them and are free for this moment of
time of all earthly cares and worries.

There is only calm and peace and the feeling of space and light.

VISUALISATION NO. 1 - CLOUDS

NOW Read the passage again.

PLAY THE AUDIO

Afterwards

Please take your time sitting up. While you are putting your shoes back on, may I just remind you to practice the breathing technique during the week ahead and before reading Chapter II and experiencing a second relaxation session.

CHAPTER II

STRESS IN THE CITY

Three quarters of the population of westernised nations now live in cities and suburbs. The cities possess many desirable qualities - they allow us to centralise public services, they give us access to a great many people in our business world, they are host to the great institutions of banking, insurance and the share markets, and they also generate an energy of their own, which can be experienced by anyone getting off an early morning commuter train at one of the city termini. However, these good qualities are balanced by the negative aspects of city life and I intend in this Chapter to touch briefly on these and to suggest how we can all make working in and travelling to the office a more pleasant and enjoyable experience.

First of all, let us consider what it is about city life that differentiates it from life anywhere else. Well that is fairly obvious - it is the density of the people working a very small area, high density leads to crowding and crowding leads to stress. There are quite marked cultural difference in how man reacts to crowding. For example the French, Italians, Greeks, Arabs and Japanese have a much higher tolerance for public crowding than Englishmen, Germans and Scandinavians and many Americans. High density in American and European cities is rarely above 180 persons for each $2^1/_2$ acres, whereas in Hong Kong some tenement districts equal 800 persons for the same area. Despite these exceptional figures for tolerance of crowding, experiments by psychologists have shown that when crowding exceeds the cultural limit or operates over an extended period of time, stress will be felt. We can all tolerate and often enjoy being part of a football crowd, at a social event or attending a business exhibition or conference, providing this is for a limited time period. If it were to continue indefinitely this close contact with our fellowman or woman would cease to be enjoyable.

I should perhaps mention that women have been found to be more tolerant of crowding than men and, when they are in all female groups, to actually welcome close contact. Whereas men have been shown to react aggressively when forced into close contact with each other.

Researchers have shown that this aggression is linked with the concept of the invasion of personal space, which in turn is linked with the instinct for territory and dominance inherited from the animal kingdom.

The way we attempt to cope with crowded situations is to withdraw physically, mentally and emotionally. To try to turn ourselves into a non-person. This can be observed very easily in the rush hour on the tube train, when close physical proximity is unavoidable but the degree of discomfort is disguised as one looks along the rows of completely expressionless faces.

Let us now look at the checklist I have prepared on how to avoid City stress.

CHECK LIST

1. GIVE YOURSELF TIME

Always allow plenty of time for yourself at the beginning of the day.

The way we start the day can have its effect throughout the whole of the following 24 hours, so it is important that we give ourselves an unhurried and calm period between rising from bed and getting into the car or train for work. To begin with we must allow for certain basic human functions and the first usually occurs shortly after breakfast in the morning. If we are so hurried that we cannot even stop for a cup of tea let alone something to eat it is unlikely that our digestive and alimentary system is going to work correctly that day.

If this becomes routine - missing breakfast - and dashing out of the house every morning - in a panic about missing the train or worrying about a business deal - there can be some very nasty complications which can develop in our alimentary system which may require surgery later in life.

Allowing yourself plenty of time in the morning cannot be emphasised too much. A leisurely start with a light breakfast, followed by some form of exercise before getting into the car or catching the train will pay off later when business decisions have to be made.

2. DO NOT OVER SCHEDULE

Do not over-schedule - quality of work and performance - rather than quantity alone.

One of the characteristic traits of the harassed business executive is that he or she is constantly looking at the time.
(*Page 20* - The Type A Personality - covered in Chapter VI)

Of course we all know that it is impossible to get through the day without some routine which, of course, inevitably means time tabling ourselves. But we must remember that we are not robots, which can be programmed to fill in every available moment with efficient productivity.

That extra appointment fitted in at the last moment is not productive if you are already tired, as your concentration will be low and you are more likely to miss some important point, which will lead to another appointment having to be made in the future.

3. RELAX WHEN TRAVELLING

If you are delayed when travelling - practice the breathing and relaxation exercises I covered in Chapter I, and instead of getting more tense and irritable you will find that either the delay is not as long as you anticipated, or that you can spend the time deciding how to best deal with the consequences of the delay. Usually it is not merely the physical discomfort of a delay that stresses us (i.e. waiting on a cold railway platform for a non-existent train) but how the delay is going to affect our timetable of the day's engagements.

THE TYPE 'A' PERSONALITY

For the traveller on public transport it has to be said that for their ultimate good health a philosophical attitude is really a must. We all know how frustrating it is to stand waiting for the train or taxi that never arrives or arrives so late that we miss our appointment. But once you have taken the obvious step of contacting the office and have asked your secretary to make the necessary apologies and rearrange your diary, a deep breath and working through the relaxation programme is far better than fuming and tensing up. As long as you have done all that you can do to minimise the consequences of the delay it is foolish to wear yourself out with worry.

4. THE DRIVER

For the car driver the position is a little better, since he or she does at least have control over the means of transport and, provided it is serviced regularly and maintained in good condition there should be no problems on starting, except in bad weather such as snow and frost.

However it is, of course, once the car is on the road that problems begin, particularly in the rush hour, and the business executive sitting in a traffic jam may well wonder whether they should have let the train take the strain. But even in these circumstances, the driver can mitigate the effects of stop start driving and frustrating delays.

When you have to stop and it will be for at least a couple of minutes - at traffic lights or in a queue of traffic - allow your hands to relax, breathe deeply in, release it and at the same time allow your shoulders to drop down and back. Repeat this at least twice depending on the circumstances and you will find the tension created by driving will disappear.

It is important to reduce the tension of driving as studies have shown that blood pressure levels rise when we drive, blood lipid levels (fat molecules in the blood) are also increased and this can be shown by taking the blood before and after a long car journey, particularly if such a journey is hurried.

Blood taken before the journey separates into a solid precipitate and clear plasma. After a long journey the plasma separates turbid and cloudy and when viewed under a microscope, is full of fats.

Of course a properly adjusted seat with enough leg room and lumbar support will also alleviate unnecessary tension in the legs, shoulders and lower back and an non-aggressive attitude to driving is essential. A radio is a good idea provided you don't keep it permanently tuned to the financial news bulletins so that the tension of driving is compounded by worry about business decisions. Some light popular music or classical CDs will do your body and driving much more good.

DO NOT UNDER ANY CIRCUMSTANCES
PLAY THE RELAXATION AUDIO
WHILST DRIVING

5. CONSIDER FLEXI-TIME

If there are real problems with travelling for you and your staff why not consider the system called Flexi-time. It has been used now for some years by many companies, large and small and it appears to work quite successfully with no loss in efficiency.

If your work means that you have to make regular telephone calls to parts of the world that are in a different time zone to yourself, don't try to work a 12-14 hour day just to cover the calls but instead work out a rota with colleagues so you each do a normal 8 hour day but covering different time periods.

6. TAKE REGULAR REST BREAKS AT WORK

Once at work, remember again that you are not a robot. You need to take the regular breaks, to break the onset of fatigue and also to refuel the body to keep the blood sugar level topped up and to take in liquid to keep the kidneys functioning properly

It is essential therefore to stretch these upper arm and shoulder muscles and also to allow the leg muscles to work after periods of sedentary work. The Japanese custom of workers and management exercising regularly during the day to music may seem strange to our western way of thinking but it has a good scientific basis, and does benefit productivity and reduce sickness.

In the same way that the muscles need to be worked to eliminate static loading on them, those parts of our nervous system which we use constantly at work, i.e. the eyes, ears and brain also need a short break.

The human eye for example was not designed to spend hours at a time gazing at a flickering computer monitor; neither were our ears designed to function at the decibel level of many city streets and offices. Our brains, which are still more complicated than any technological advance also, need rest and recuperation.

If your work involves constant social interaction through meetings etc. then 20 minutes peace and quiet will do you good and quieten down the nervous system. Conversely if you spend much of your time working alone, 20 minutes socialising with colleagues will relax you more. It is a question of getting the balance right.

Just remember that, despite what we sometimes like to believe, we are not indispensable and even if you do stop for essential breaks the department, division and company will not come to an abrupt end.

THE OFFICE ENVIRONMENT

Environmental conditions affect us all and as we spend many hours at work it is sensible to look at those features of our office environment which can contribute to our wellbeing or otherwise and these are noise, heating and ventilation, lighting, equipment and furniture.

1. NOISE

Not all noise is unpleasant. Many noises such as those in the countryside, the murmur of a stream, the rustling of leaves, and birdsong, are considered therapeutic and pleasant. Similarly waves breaking on a beach and the lapping of water against the side of a boat can be quite soporific.

However certain types of noise can affect people and reduce their working efficiency. The factors which are most important are noise level and frequency (high frequency affects more people), randomly occurring or unusual noise, and the context in which it is heard.

In the office no noise at all would not give the impression of a productive commercial company but too high a noise level reduces productivity and impedes communication. Most modern offices should be designed to keep noise levels to a minimum but it is always a good idea to check on this with a specialist to see if improvements could be made.

Noise is usually bearable if it is short lived, it is the incessant wearing down effects of constant noise, and it doesn't have to be very loud, which is stressful.

Young people have a greater tolerance for noise, which is understandable since they seek higher levels of arousal and stimulation than older people.

However toleration doesn't mean that no harm is done and continuing exposure to above normal noise levels will produce measurable damage to hearing by the time middle age is reached.

Many people are surprised when they are told just how noisy a combination of telephones, computer terminals, telexes and photocopiers can be and in many offices they will exceed recommended levels.

Noise is measured in decibels, which are units of sound pressure level. A maximum of 40 dB is needed for ordinary speech at 8-10 feet but in a busy office with other equipment operating, this will be exceeded if you are to be heard clearly and unfortunately once one person raises their voice, others follow and the general level increases.

The recommended levels are:

private office	25-35 dB
medium office	40-45 dB
accounts / typing pool	33-65 dB

Note: Levels in excess of 90 dB cause permanent damage to hearing.

Noise causes the body's arousal system to be activated and when this reaches beyond the comfort zone performance and productivity suffer. Studies have shown that productivity can increase by more than 50% when noise and distraction are reduced.

2. HEATING AND VENTILATION

The statutory requirements for offices are 61.8 F minimum with maximum temperature dependent on humidity. Many modern office blocks should theoretically have been designed with the optimum comfort for the occupants, however there are still those where the conditions could be improved. A comfortable office atmosphere is essential as extreme heat, cold, dampness or dryness will cause even the most enthusiastic employee's performance to suffer.

The majority of people when questioned say that they find temperatures of 21-24 C the most comfortable. Overheating in an office leads to weariness and sleepiness, loss of performance and increased liability to errors. Overcooling induces restlessness, which reduces alertness and concentration, particularly on mental tasks.

The humidity of the air is also important. If the relative humidity of the air falls below 30% there is the danger of too dry an atmosphere. This can often occur as the tendency has been for higher and higher temperatures indoors during the period of the year when buildings are heated and this has led to lower and lower values of relative humidity.

Excessive dryness of the air in heated rooms can lead to catarrhal complaints and chronic irritation of the nasal and bronchial passages. This increases the likelihood of infections and relative humidity below 30% is unhygienic. Therefore this is one area where getting a correct assessment of the office environment could increase everyone's comfort and decrease sickness.

THE FRESH AIR DEBATE

In the interests of health it is advisable to apply a NO SMOKING rule in the office. Whatever the objections from smokers, non-smokers have a right to fresh air and it is of course essential for those with respiratory complaints. This is an area where top management should, but often don't, unfortunately, set the lead. But whatever you feel about the issue there are now cases where employees have taken legal action against employers as a result of passive smoking (breathing in other people's cigarette smoke).

VENTILATION SYSTEMS

Since the tragic deaths of people who have died as a result of contracting Legionnaires disease, which has been traced back to badly maintained air conditioning systems, companies have become aware how important it is so ensure that any ventilation system is correctly monitored.

This is after all only common sense, since any system which is circulating air around many people day after day can so easily lead to the spread of cold viruses and bacteria if the filtering system is not properly monitored.

3. LIGHTING

Modern light sources are broadly of two kinds, electric filament lamps and fluorescent tubes. Fluorescent tubes are the main source of lighting in offices as they give off three or four times more light than filament lamps. The advantages of the fluorescent tube is that it can be manufactured to give off different kinds of coloured light, warm light, white light or blue light. They also do not produce as much glare as filament lamps.

The disadvantage is that because they operate with alternating current fluorescent tubes flicker, 50 Hz in the U.K. and this flicker is above that noticed by the human eye. However when tubes become old or defective they develop a slow flicker especially at the ends and this can cause, after a period time, problems with the eyes and headaches.

With many of the new lighting systems, the problems have been solved but if you do develop headaches after a new system has been installed, check with others in the office before making an appointment with the optician.

If you do a lot of reading and wear glasses, or work at a VDU remember that your eyes are under constant strain, especially during winter months when natural daylight is reduced. Try to leave the office for at least 30 minutes during the day to give your eyes a rest and you should not work continuously at a VDU screen, a ten minute rest each hour is a minimum

4. OFFICE LAYOUT - EQUIPMENT AND FURNITURE

If you have the opportunity to choose the type of seating, desk or workstations you will be using remember to give ergonomic considerations priority over purely aesthetic or status factors. It is also sensible to take advantage of any devices which reduce strain when using the telephone - since holding the arm, neck and head in one position for any length of time will cause tension.

The recommended heights for office desks used without a typewriter or word processor should be:

men: 74-78 cm

women: 70-74 cm

assuming that the chairs are fully adjustable and footrests are available for short people for typing the table height should be 69 cms for men and 65 for women.

The advantages of a sitting position over a standing position for the body are:

a. the weight is taken off the legs
b. ability to avoid unnatural body posture
c. reduced energy consumption
d. fewer demands on the blood system

Against these are the disadvantages of (sitter's stomach) curvature of the spine and compression of the colon and lungs.

Many people suffer back problems sometime in life and the most common is disc problems. It has been found that to avoid and to help disc problems the angle of the seat (in relation to the ground) should be 10 degrees and the angle between the seat and the backrest should be 115-120 degrees. A lumber pad 5cm thick also lowers disc pressure and backache.

As you spend as much time sitting in a chair as you do lying in bed, it is as well to get as good a chair as a comfortable mattress.

Seat heights should be adjusted for each person.

Open-plan offices or private offices?

Often people do not have any input into which type of office they prefer. However where open plan offices have been introduced it has been necessary to provide some kind of screening around each workstation, as the need for some degree of privacy is high, and also to prevent unnecessary distraction.

It should also be remembered that as people mature they feel a greater need for privacy than the young who can adapt more quickly to higher noise levels and interruptions to work.

REVIEW OF CHAPTERS I AND II

Over the last two chapters I have attempted to explain how both our physiology and the environment in which we live and work affect each other and how we can reinforce positive influences and reduce negative ones.

The material in both these chapters applies to everyone and that is why I have specified that these should be read first and if possible with a week's break between each chapter. This is so that you can think about what I have written during the week and also to allow time for practicing the relaxation technique.

If you were learning to drive you would not expect to learn everything in one session, but would first be taught the basics about starting the car etc. and would over a period of time gradually build up your driving skill with knowledge and experience. It is the same with learning to relax. It can be done but like anything else it is best learnt one step at a time and slowly building to the point where it becomes automatic.

So before you read the Visualisation page at the end of this Chapter, I would like you to practice the breathing technique I described in Chapter I.

BREATHING TECHNIQUE

Remember this technique is designed to regulate your breathing - and as your breathing becomes calm and regular so also will you.

Now with your hands on each side of your abdomen breathe in slowly through your nose and then slowly out again. Feel the abdomen rise and fall under your hands. As you breathe in through your nose count 1, 2 to yourself and as you breathe out count 1, 2, 3.

Do it NOW

Good, you should feel your abdomen rise on the inward breath and fall on the outward breath.

If you are ready to begin a relaxation session, turn to the visualisation on *page 32* and read it twice.

The Business of Learning to Relax

*Imagine a cold winter's afternoon, with a bitter wind blowing
and the rain spattering the windows,
but you are inside in the warm, sitting in a deep comfortable
armchair gazing into the flickering flames of an open fire.*

*The coal and logs are piled high so that the flames are
bright and strong and there is a satisfying crackle as the driest twigs
burn and the occasional sizzle where the sap from the logs
evaporates in the heat.*

*You can smell the smoke, some of it quite fragrant -especially
if pine is being burnt and you watch the flames dancing
next to each other.*

*There is no other light in the room and
gradually what daylight there is fades and it becomes dark outside
and the only light is that given out by the fire.*

*The flickering flames throw their shadows out onto
the ceiling and the walls and the room becomes alive
with the reflected light.*

*On the mantelpiece the clock is ticking gently
and its sound is only broken by the swoosh of ash falling into the grate.*

*The rhythm of the clock and the pattering of the rain on the window
are soothing in their own way
and the slowly dying firelight combines in making you feel very sleepy.*

In fact if you stayed by the fire any longer you might well fall fast asleep.

VISUALISATION NO. 2 - FIRELIGHT

NOW Read the passage again.

PLAY THE AUDIO

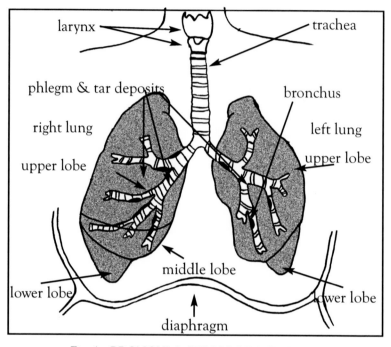

Fig. 4. - BRONCHI & LUNGS OF A SMOKER

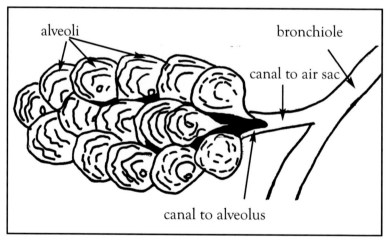

Fig. 5. - AIR-SAC WITH ALVEOLI x 100

CHAPTER III

SMOKING, ALCOHOL AND DRUG ADDICTION

In this Chapter I am going to talk about three of the crutches we use when we are stressed. I will be briefly outlining the dangers they pose to our health and I will be suggesting ways in which we can successfully give up these crutches and replace them by deep relaxation technique instead.

SMOKING

Let us start with the smoking habit. We all know that smoking is not good for our health but to remind you I will refer to three reports by the Royal College of Physicians in 1962, 1971 and 1977 which all came down heavily against cigarette smoking. They cited it as one of the major contributory factors in lung cancer, heart disease, hypertension and bronchitis.

If you look at *page 34 Fig.4* you will see the diagram of the respiratory system reproduced again, but this time it is that of a smoker.

The air we breathe in travels down our airway, the trachea, which divides into two bronchi which lead into the lungs one on each side. Each bronchus gives rise to several main branches, which divide repeatedly until, at the final stage, microscopic bronchioles are reached. Each bronchiole gives rise to three or four branches and each branch leads to an air-sac about 1 mm long with numerous pouches called alveoli leading from it. (You can see this enlarged by 100 times on *page 34 Fig.5*) It is through the walls of the alveoli that the gas exchange between the air we breathe and the blood that circulates in our bodies takes place.

When the alveoli dilate they press tightly against blood vessels and oxygen in the air dissolves in the moisture lining the alveoli and through their thin walls into the blood where it is carried by the red corpuscles around the body. Conversely carbon dioxide is passed out from the blood into the alveoli and is then breathed out. This exchange of gases is dependent on healthy tissues in the lungs and any foreign substance will adversely affect it.

The tar in cigarettes has been blamed for many a smoker's cough and you will see that the black ovals in the bronchi represent the plaques of phlegm and catarrh.

If there is a change in the balance of gas exchange, there will be a build up of impure gas in the body with reduced oxygen consumption by the blood corpuscles, leading to fatigue. The eventual break down of the respiratory system can lead to fluid leaking into the lungs causing emphysema. There is also the danger of cancerous growths within the lung tissues. If you take the pulse rate of someone before they inhale cigarette smoke and then once they have inhaled, you will find that there is an increase in the pulse rate, and this is being repeated countless times every day by a smoker.

With so much evidence of damage caused by smoking why do people find it hard to give up? This is because the nicotine in the cigarette is an addictive drug, and addictions are hard to break. However we know that it can be broken, in the same way that addicts of other drugs can break their habit, but it takes effort, willpower and, above all, commitment.

Why do you smoke?

It can be from HABIT, for PLEASURE, to REDUCE TENSION, or to CONFORM

Let us look at each of these reasons and how they can be answered.

(a) HABIT

How can you combat this? The key lies in changing your routine, at least as far as it is affected by smoking.

Change your routine a little in order to break up the patterns of behaviour. For example if you have the habit of always smoking when you have a tea or coffee break, try changing to a soft drink, fruit juice or milk while you are breaking the smoking habit.

If you always purchase a packet of cigarettes from a certain kiosk each morning, either take a different route to avoid it, or buy sweets, a soft drink or newspaper instead. Chewing gum, while not always a socially desirable habit, can be very beneficial during the first few weeks.

Instead of that early morning cigarette take a few deep breaths and practice a few gentle exercises. If you feel breathless remind yourself why this is so, the result of smoking.

Other people have got used to you smoking, especially fellow smokers, so to prevent them automatically offering you a cigarette, put out one of the non-smoking cards (available from the Health Education Council) on your desk.

With no smoking on trains, no smoking on buses and a ban on smoking in public places being introduced in the U.K. this is the right time to stop your smoking habit.

(b) PLEASURE

The second reason people smoke is for pleasurable oral stimulation. This type of smoker gets a purely sensual pleasure from smoking. He or she needs to put something in the mouth to give a pleasurable feeling. This can be traced back, according to psychoanalysts, to childhood. Anyway, it seems that the cigarette will have initially to be replaced with something else - gum, peppermints, and if you are at home, carrots, celery, or whatever you feel will help.

(c) TO REDUCE TENSION

Of course many people admit to smoking purely to reduce stress and tension and to combat fatigue. This is a fallacy since cigarette smoking does not actually energise the body but the nicotine drug gives a temporary lift, which fools us into thinking that we are operating more effectively. That is why we get withdrawal symptoms when we try to give up and become irritable and edgy.

The effect is only temporary and once our bodies are released from the nicotine craving we can really benefit from the positive effects of not smoking.

(d) CONFORMITY

In an age when it has been popular to "be an individual" and "do your own thing" there are still those people who despite their own private misgivings, go along with a practice because it is the fashion, it appears "macho" or some other group pressure. It is surely a sign of maturity when you can take responsibility for your own life and in particular your health.

Having looked at the reasons why people smoke, let us now look at the reasons why you should break the smoking habit and what you will gain.

Reasons for NOT smoking:

1. Lung cancer kills over 38,000 people in the U.K. each year One person every 14 minutes. Cigarette smoking is one of the major contributory factors in lung cancer.

2. The average smoker is twice as likely to die of a heart attack than a non-smoker. Cigarette smoking is one of the major contributory factors in heart disease.

3. The average smoker is more likely to develop chronic bronchitis, which kills over 24,000 people a year. Cigarette smoking is one of the major contributory factors in bronchitis and chest complaints.

4. This year 50,000 people will die before their time because of smoking.

5. Every cigarette smoked shortens your life by $5^1/2$ minutes.

6. Out of every 1,000 young people who smoke - six will be killed in traffic accidents - but 250 will be killed by smoking.

If you really wish to break your smoking habit, replace cigarette smoking with the relaxation technique taught in this book.

Do you really wish to stop smoking?

While you are thinking about this, read below the benefits of stopping the smoking habit.

BENEFITS TO BE GAINED from NOT smoking:

1. Less likely to develop heart disease, bronchitis or lung cancer.

2. Able to breathe more easily - enjoy sports and social activities more, this also includes sexual performance.

3. Get rid of your smoker's cough.

4. Look better, no more nicotine stained fingers and teeth. Smell nicer, breath, hair, clothes and car will no longer smell of tobacco.

5. For ladies, if you become pregnant, a better chance of a healthy baby.

6   For parents, your children will be less likely to smoke.

7   For everyone, think what you could do with the money you save, instead of burning it you could spend it on a holiday, new clothes, a new hobby, or some special occasion or treat.

When you have decided to break the smoking habit, and if it is before moving on to Chapter IV, then you should practise the relaxation technique after this Chapter and at the point on the audio track where you are allowed time.

> *"to go back and allow yourself to think about the tension in your body"*

you should repeat to yourself

> *"today I am taking the first step in breaking the smoking habit and allowing myself good health"*

If you repeat this to yourself during the relaxation session at the end of each Chapter, I am confident that you will be able to break your smoking habit by the end of the next seven weeks.

ALCOHOL

In this world there are three types of people. Those who do not like or do not drink alcohol for moral or religious reasons, the majority who enjoy the odd drink when in company as it makes us feel more relaxed and the atmosphere more friendly or at meal time when a good wine enhances the flavour of food and aids digestion, and those for who alcohol is a daily necessity which rules their lives and which may in the end cause their death.

Much research has gone into trying to identify what factors cause the moderate social drinker to become an alcoholic. To date six different types of alcoholic have been identified, together with the possible reasons for their behaviour.

Typology of Alcoholism

1. The habit drinker whose consumption of alcohol has steadily increased without them realising it until they are forced by circumstances to stop drinking, for example they have to attend hospital for another condition and find that they are experiencing withdrawal symptoms.

2. The regular drinker who although they do not appear drunk are, in fact, never totally sober and certainly can't face the day without a drink. These are usually social drinkers who like the atmosphere of the bar and the company of others.

3. Some are solitary drinkers, and these tend to be women at home, although sometimes both sexes have weekend drinking sessions but sober up for Monday morning.

4. Then there is the compulsive alcoholic who drinks until he or she is physically incapable of doing so. This type of alcoholic is the main stay of Alcoholics Anonymous.

5. Sometimes alcoholism can be symptomatic of some other disorder, such as depression. If the underlying depression can be cured then the need for alcohol will diminish.

6. The last type of alcoholic is the periodic drinker who has drinking bouts interspersed with long periods of abstinence and mere social drinking.

All these different types of alcoholics however will experience the various stages in alcoholism listed on below. If anyone recognises any of these symptoms in themselves and particularly if there are two or three then it is certainly important for them to think seriously about their consumption of alcohol and to take steps to remedy it.

The stages in excessive drinking
> More time spent drinking
> More evenings spent drinking
> Pattern of drinking changes,
>> i.e. stronger drinks, or amount increases
> Always thinking about the next drink
> Drinking to relieve tension
> Feels guilty over drinking
> Drink has become a necessity

The stages in alcoholism
> Increased tolerance
> First two or three drinks taken rapidly
> Guilt feelings
> Drinking to the point of drunkenness
> Loss of memory occur
> Frequency of amnesia increases
> Loses the capacity to regulate drinking
> Interests become narrower
> Loss of working efficiency
> Absenteeism occurs
> Drunk in the daytime
> Aggressive
> Diminished sexual drive
> Morning drinking

Always supplies of drink available
Neglect of nutrition
Cheap wine or meths
Thinking is confused
Serious illness
Suicide is a high risk

When any of the stages listed are experienced then is most likely that the mental and physical changes given below will also be taking place.

Physical changes in alcoholism

Malnutrition

Lack of appetite

Gastritis (inflammation of the stomach lining)

Cirrhosis (inflammation of the liver)

Peripheral neuritis (tingling of toes, fingers and hands leading to numbness)

Mental changes in alcoholism

Withdrawal symptoms - the shakes

Hallucinations

D.T.'s 2 - 4 days after stopping heavy drinking

Disorientation

Alcoholic epilepsy

To anyone who feels that they are on the first stages of excessive drinking I suggest that when they play the relaxation audio - at the point where I say "I want you to go back to any part of your body where you can feel any tension" you repeat to yourself.

> "I know I crave alcohol, I realise that alcohol is a poison to me, as it is a poison to me I must avoid it at all costs. In future when I feel the urge to drink alcohol I will remember that it is poison to me and I will feel sick at the thought of it passing my lips"

For the excessive drinker this MUST be repeated on a daily basis, until 28 successive alcohol free days have been accomplished and then if and when ever the need arises.

It is very easy to condemn the person who appears to be under the control of drink, but in western society the pressures on the business executive to consume alcohol during the working day are very strong. Many business deals take place in the wine bar or public house as well as the office and, although Britain is more in line with the Continent, there is still a tendency for the British to drink more spirits in smaller time periods.

There are a quarter of a million alcoholics in Britain which means that one person in every 100 is an alcoholic. Alcoholics are not typically the down and out who drinks meths and who is found in cardboard boxes under the railway arches. Company directors are 22 times more likely to develop cirrhosis of the liver but they are more fortunate in that they will probably have access to help in special private clinics. The recovery rate is 40% for those treated in groups and the average stay is 4-12 weeks. It has also been shown that the executive's spouse is also at risk from alcoholism compared with other women.

Of course heavy drinking not only affects the immediate colleagues and family of the drinker but can extend to the general public when accidents through drunk driving occur. Over 50% of road accidents are caused by drinking. Lunchtime is a particularly dangerous period since driving performance drops after lunch for up to four hours, following a heavy meal and drinks.

There are various limits given by different authorities as to how much one can drink without endangering your health. I would suggest 21 units of absolute alcohol a week as an upper limit, which is 2 pints of beer, half a bottle of wine or two doubles of gin or whisky a day. Women, with a lower body weight than men, should not exceed a maximum of 14 units of alcohol a week. But to retain a slim waistline, a clear head and healthy nervous system there is nothing wrong at all in saying NO to alcohol. It is not needed by your body and you can function perfectly well without it, if you prefer to drink fruit juice, or mineral water, just say so.

Finally it is strongly recommended that anyone who knows that they are a true alcoholic seeks professional advice and support in breaking their drinking pattern. Before any counselling can be carried out on the underlying reason for their drinking it is imperative that they "dry out" i.e. allow their body to be alcohol free for some time in order that the physical effects can be evaluated and that they have a clear mind with which to reflect on the events which started them to drink in the first instance.

There are a number of addresses of supportive agencies given on *page 48* at the end of the chapter.

Spouses of alcoholic and their families also require help and counselling and they should not be afraid to ask for this too.

DRUG ADDICTION

For many people the term drug addict brings forth a disgusted response, yet it is just like the other two addictions except whereas smoking was until fairly recently socially accepted, and alcoholism tolerated in certain classes, drug abuse because of its criminal overtones has a definite social stigma. This is because to the person in the street the term drug means illegal drugs such as cocaine, heroin or the "soft" drugs such as marijuana.

However, drugs, which are dispensed quite legally by chemists in this country also, have powerful addictive properties. In the 1960's and 70's there was a boom in the manufacture of tranquillisers and, because these were very effective at relieving anxiety and tension they were prescribed rather too enthusiastically by many doctors. The results were that many people became permanently addicted to such drugs. In those days these were mainly housewives. More recently in a 1980 study it was revealed that 30% of male executives and 40% of woman executives were taking stress relieving drugs.

Now many of the new generation of doctors are realising that these prescribed drugs must be treated with caution and a closer watch is being kept on request for repeat prescriptions. Obviously if you are being prescribed drugs to deal with anxiety and tension or for insomnia you will only wish to take this for the minimum time required. Tranquillisers should only be taken for a maximum 2-4 weeks and even then the risk of dependence exists, so long term use is not to be recommended. Certain of the benzodiazepine drugs such as Dalmane and Normison marketed as sleeping pills are only effective for between three and twelve days, so the long term use of these is also contraindicated.

It is far better to calm the body naturally with a method that has no side effects.

Hard drugs

It is impossible to cover this subject in a few paragraphs but I will just therefore mention the salient points on drug abuse.

The first thing to remember about drug taking is that it is a physical addiction which alters body chemistry and therefore thought processes and behaviour. It provides, in the initial stages, a lift or high, a means of escape from everyday life, from the pressures that life presents.

The young have always been the easy prey of those who peddle drugs and, with rising unemployment and the influx of cheaper and more dangerous drugs over the last few years, drug addiction has increased in the United Kingdom as in other countries. But it is not just the teenager and misunderstood adolescent who turns to drugs in ignorance. Today there are many people in their twenties and thirties who are addicted to hard drugs, professional and affluent people who have become involved in drugs through social and business contacts. Luckily for them they have the money to pay for special treatment and clinics have been set up specifically to deal with type of addict.

The drugs, which most commonly lead to addiction, are opium and its derivatives, morphine and heroin, cocaine, cannabis, barbiturates and amphetamines. Once addiction has developed, a physical dependency on the drug rapidly follows as a result biochemical changes, which produce an incessant craving for the drug. The withdrawal of the drug produces such intense and painful physiological reactions that there is a chance that the addict may die without medical treatment and supervision. Therefore it is ESSENTIAL that anyone attempting to come off any drugs (prescriptive or otherwise) should seek medical advice.

The relaxation audio can be used an aid in alleviating tension and distress following the withdrawal stage of drugs and can be of benefit together with the support of counselling. Counselling is probably the most effective means of combating drug abuse, along with efforts to restrict the ease of obtaining such drugs on the open market.

The problems of solvent abuse, glue sniffing and inhalation of other aerosol sprays is mainly centred around school age children who become involved in these activities through boredom, experimentation or peer pressure. Parents should always be vigilant of any change in their children's behaviour and for any evidence of sniffing. It is important to be as well informed as possible about the problem as well-intentioned action such as chasing a youngster who has been seen sniffing can bring about their death, due to heart failure. Over 100 teenagers a year die from solvent abuse.

On *page 48 and 49* there is a list of agencies who can help with the problem of drug addiction and solvent abuse.

On *page 50* is Visualisation No. 3. This has been specifically prepared for use by anyone who is attempting to break an addictive habit.

For maximum benefit it should be used at a time when the reader is not 'high' on drugs or alcohol, and for the smoker at the point where he or she has decided to break their smoking habit.

Read the Visualisation twice as with Nos. 1 and 2 and then play the audio.

USEFUL ADDRESSES FOR FURTHER INFORMATION
ON SMOKING, ALCOHOLISM & DRUGS

Smoking
ASH
109 Gloucester Place
London W1H 3PH
www.ash.org.uk
Tel: 0207 935 3519

Alcoholism
Alcohol Advice Centres
see telephone book for your area

Alcoholics Anonymouse
PO BOX 1
10 Toft Green
York YO1 7ND
www.alcholics-anonymous.org.uk
Tel: 0845 769 7555 (National Helpline)

Drugs
Drug Scope
40 Bermondsey Street
London SE1 3UD
www.drugscope.org.uk
Tel: 0207 928 9500

Re-Solv,
The Society for the Prevention Solvent and Volatile Substance Abuse
30A High Street
Stone
Staffs, ST15 8AW
www.re-solv.org.uk
Tel: 01785 817885

Lifeline
101-103 Oldham Street
Manchester
M4 1LW
Tel: 0161 834 7160

VISUALISATION NO. 3 - THE TUNNEL

Imagine you are in a tunnel, it is cold and dark and musty.
As you look over your shoulder, all you can see is darkness
not a chink of light.
You feel very frightened, very alone, very abandoned and sick with fear.

However, as you screw up your eyes you see a pinpoint of light ahead in the blackness. At
first you are not sure if it is really there but
as you stumble forward, your eyes focus again and, yes,
it is really there, a small dot of light.

You begin to move forward, cautiously at first, stumbling over obstacles
on the ground which you cannot even see,
and you put out your hands on to the walls to save yourself from falling.
The walls feel cold and damp to your touch. Yet with every step the light grows until it
is the size of a dinner plate.

It is the end of the tunnel and that means there is a way out
of the cold and darkness.
Your heart and spirit lift, you know now that there is a point in going on, so you continue
your uncomfortable and painful journey
towards the tunnel entrance.

Soon you can see the colour green and make out some vegetation and the light level grows
so that you can see the daylight shining off the path leading out of the tunnel.
A few more steps and you are at the tunnel entrance, framed in its arch and gazing out
into the brightness of the world outside you breathe in
the fresh clean air.
You raise your arms and stretch them out in the daylight.

Turning round you look back at the tunnel, remember its coldness and darkness and vow
never to enter that place again.

VISUALISATION NO. 3 - THE TUNNEL

NOW Read the passage again.

PLAY THE AUDIO

Recommended Weight Ranges for Men and Women

MEN						
Height no shoes	small frame		medium frame		large frame	
metres	kilos		kilos		kilos	
1.55	46.70	50.00	49.17	53.75	52.50	58.75
1.57	47.90	51.67	50.42	55.42	53.76	58.75
1.60	49.17	52.50	51.67	56.67	55.02	61.66
1.63	50.42	53.75	52.92	57.92	56.25	63.33
1.65	51.67	55.42	54.17	59.58	57.50	65.85
1.68	53.33	57.00	55.83	61.25	59.17	67.92
1.70	55.00	58.75	57.50	63.33	61.25	70.00
1.73	56.66	60.41	59.16	65.83	62.91	70.84
1.75	58.33	62.50	61.00	67.50	65.42	72.52
1.78	60.00	65.00	62.50	69.58	67.10	74.54
1.80	61.66	66.66	65.00	70.83	69.17	76.64
1.83	63.66	68.33	66.66	72.92	70.00	78.72
1.86	65.83	70.42	68.33	75.00	72.10	80.00
1.88	67.50	71.25	70.42	77.05	74.17	83.00
1.91	69.77	72.92	71.67	79.10	75.80	85.00
WOMEN						
1.50	40.83	44.58	43.58	48.35	46.67	53.34
1.53	42.51	45.83	44.58	49.59	47.93	54.60
1.55	43.75	47.09	45.83	50.84	49.19	55.83
1.58	45.00	48.35	47.09	52.50	50.42	57.50
1.60	46.25	49.59	48.35	54.18	52.09	59.17
1.63	47.51	51.25	50.00	56.25	53.76	60.85
1.65	49.19	52.92	51.67	57.92	55.44	62.53
1.68	50.84	54.60	53.34	59.59	57.12	65.00
1.70	52.50	56.28	55.02	61.27	58.75	66.68
1.73	54.18	56.70	56.70	62.95	60.43	68.78
1.75	55.86	58.38	58.33	65.42	62.11	70.00
1.78	57.54	60.06	60.01	67.10	63.79	72.10

CHAPTER IV

DIET AND EXERCISE

In this chapter I am going to talk about keeping our bodies in as good a condition as possible through healthy balanced eating and by taking sufficient exercise.

To begin with I want you to consider these three facts.

1. 40% of all British adults are overweight.

2. The risk of death increases by 13% for every 10% extra bodyweight above the average for height and build.

3. Each negative health factor such as smoking and obesity becomes multiplied by the other, therefore the individual with a threefold risk from smoking and a threefold risk from obesity is nine times more likely to suffer from coronary heart disease than his slim non-smoking friend.

DIET

Business executives are particularly at risk from obesity since their occupation is primarily a sedentary one, to which is added two to three hours spent sitting in a car or train getting to and from work. Add to this a generous expense account and business lunches and it is very easy to let the extra few kilograms in weight turn over time into several kilograms.

There are of course those lucky individuals whose body frame and metabolism allows them to eat freely without putting on excess weight but for the majority of us, especially once we are over 30, it is necessary to plan our eating if we want to avoid the problems caused later in life by overweight.

On *page 52* you will see the recommended weight ranges for men and women according to height. The generous range given for a particular height is to take account of small, medium and large body frames.

A good guide to body frame is the size of the hands and feet. So if you usually take a large size in gloves or shoes you would be considered to have a large body frame.

No doubt you each have a pair of scales at home so you can check out your own weight and see whether you need to lose any weight or not. If you do weigh with ordinary indoor clothes on allow 1kg for these.

Except when we are unusually stressed most people who use their brain in their occupation do not need to eat as much as those who are burning up calories using their muscle power.

A middle-aged man needs between 2,500 and 3,500 calories a day and women between 2,000 and 3,000. Food is not the only necessity of life, we must drink up to four pints of liquid a day and preferably just plain water. Our bodies are made up of 60% water and it is essential that we keep our kidneys flushed through to rid the body of any impurities. With women, of course, the percentage of water in the body varies with the menstrual cycle and this can cause a bloated feeling and increase in body weight of up to 7lbs in the week preceding menstruation.

Below I have listed the Do's and Don'ts of Healthy eating.

DO'S AND DON'TS OF HEALTHY EATING

DO :
1. Eat less red meat
2. Drink low fat milk
3. Grill food
4. Choose low fat margarine
5. Eat less cheese and butter
6. Eat more fibre - bran
7. Eat more fruit and vegetables

DON'T
1. Choose foods high in excess sugar
2. Add sugar to tea and coffee
3. Add extra salt to meals
4. Fry food
5. Nibble between meals

6. Rush eating

7. Drink excessively - both alcohol and
   commercial fruit drinks (except low calorie) are high in calories

You may be wondering why we have to cut down on fat in our diet, when most people think that it is the sugar and starch which makes us overweight. This is a fallacy - a fatty food like butter and margarine has ten times as many calories as the same quantity of starchy food like potatoes. Any excess fat or oil in our food is turned immediately into flab. Another reason for cutting down on fat is because of its effect on your heart. Doctors believe that one of the causes of heart disease is the concentration of fat-like substances in the blood stream, one of which is cholesterol. This is best reduced by limiting the amount of fat eaten in the diet, particularly the 'saturated' or animal fats.

You should try to replace meat meals with fish wherever possible. But grill, smoke or poach the fish, rather than fry. Oily fish can be eaten sparingly and there is evidence now that fish oil actually has a beneficial effect on the heart. Of course there are those people who are vegetarians or who cannot tolerate fish of any kind, they can always compensate by eating more of the pulses.

There are many, many diet books on the market but in my opinion the best way to take off excess weight and to keep it off is to reprogram your eating habits, to fit your lifestyle and attempt steady weight loss of $^{1}/_{2}$-1 kilogram a week until you reach your goal weight. Then to keep on with the program, introducing different foods in small amounts, whilst keeping a record of any fluctuation in weight. Crash diets are a waste of time and can be very dangerous particularly if there is an existing medical condition.

When the urge to overeat comes on think about the positive aspects of losing weight, being able to climb stairs without getting winded, fitting into seats on trains, planes and cars more comfortably, more choice and less hassle when buying clothes, being able to choose younger and more fashionable styles, and from the business and social point of view, a slim trim figure gives a youthful appearance regardless of actual age see *page 56*.

While you are trying to lose weight you should be considering a suitable form of exercise regime to adopt as well and once you are down to the recommended weight you can then start exercising in order to keep the body trim.

Do not try to do hard exercise however while you are still very overweight as you will only be putting the body under more strain, better to keep to gentle exercise until you have lost the weight by sensible eating and then start to tone up.

IF YOU HAVE ANY MEDICAL CONDITION, ARE ON ANY MEDICATION, OR ARE 10 KILOGRAMS OR MORE OVERWEIGHT SEEK YOUR DOCTOR'S ADVICE BEFORE DIETING AND EXERCISING.

DIET AND EXERCISE FOR GOOD HEALTH

EXERCISE

Regular exercise is one of the best ways of keeping the body fit and supple. It does not mean performing a Jane Fonda aerobic workout every morning or attempting Olympic standard run round the local park. The key word is regular. A brisk walk to and from the railway station of 15 to 20 minutes is just as effective and easier to keep to regularly.

If you have a bicycle why not try cycling to the station instead of getting your partner to drive you there every morning. Swimming is a very good form of exercise especially for those who have joint problems such as arthritis or rheumatism, since the body is kept weightless and there is no strain on the ligaments.

For those over 40 if you have always kept up an active sport such as badminton, tennis, football, squash etc. then carry on but remember that you will naturally slow down as you get older and if you try to compete with younger, fitter men and women you are just asking for trouble. Why not change to another sport where judgement and accuracy are more important than sheer physical strength or stamina.

Now let us look at the DO'S and DON'TS of healthy exercise.

DO'S AND DON'TS OF HEALTHY EXERCISE

DO

Check with your doctor if

1. You are more than 10 kilograms overweight

2. You have asthma or are bronchitic

3. You have been diagnosed as having high blood pressure or heart disease

4. You smoke more than 20 cigarettes daily

5. If you have back, joint or vein problems

6. You have any serious medical condition which may be affected

ALL EXERCISES TO BE DONE SLOWLY AND GENTLY

Head rolling right - left left - right 5 repeats

upwards & downward stretch
5 repeats

arms circling backwards &
forwards 5 repeats each

side stretch right side stretch
left 5 repeats each

squats (keep back straight)
5 repeats

trunk rotation 5 to left
5 to right

final forward stretch

Fig. 6. - A GENTLE WARM-UP ROUTINE

DON'T

1. Overdo things take it easily at first, always warm up before any strenuous exercise

2. Skimp on correct kit particularly footwear when jogging

3. Exercise after a heavy meal always allow2 hours before swimming

4. Exercise when recovering from a viral infection such as flu, allow the body the normal recovery time

5. Exercise your heart more than 60-80% of its capacity

As a guide no one over 40 should exercise so strongly that his or her pulse rate goes over 120. Although there will be exceptions to this, professional athletes and those who teach or exercise as part of their work, dancers etc.

Below I have given an easy formula for working this out according to age.

Equation   *Maximum pulse rate minus your age x % = pulse rate training level*

e.g.   220 - 40 x 80/100 = 144 Very fit
220 - 40 x 60/100 = 108 Unfit

Exercise facilities for the business executive in London have not been easily obtained in the past but with more interest in health and fitness over the last decade more and more gymnasiums are being introduced.

In the office itself it is possible to do simple stretching exercises to help to release the tension in the neck and shoulders and lower back which is caused by sitting at a desk for a long time. These are given diagrammatically on *page 58 Fig 6*. The chief drawback to doing these exercises is that we in the West are so inhibited and are afraid of looking silly. In Japan however the business executive is encouraged to take part in exercise breaks during the day and is helped by the accompaniment of music fed through the office intercom.

EATING DISORDERS

In the last few years since I started my courses there has been a good deal of press coverage and interest in eating disorders. Although these have existed in the past like many other problems in life they have not been recognised by the public until there has been a focus by the media.

Eating disorders are like the problems of smoking, alcoholism and drug addiction and combination of the pressures of the environment combined with effects of events in an individual's life.

The two commonest eating disorders are compulsive eating and obsessive weight loss, this second disorder is split into two groups; anorexia nervosa and bulimia.

You will note that I have not listed the condition of obesity under eating disorders. This is because a person may be 20% more than the recommended bodyweight for their size and frame and therefore be obese but they are not necessarily suffering from an eating disorder.

Obesity is the result not the cause and the cause may be a disturbance in metabolism, due to another medical condition, or because of a side effect of medication i.e. steroids, and many people who are obese are not huge eaters. Therefore if you are overweight and know that you eat sensibly and keep to a calorific intake suitable for your lifestyle, then you should seek your doctor's advice to check whether at your present weight your blood pressure and cholesterol level are satisfactory.

However if you answer YES to any of the questions below then you may well be a compulsive eater.

1. Do you regularly buy food secretly just for yourself?

2. Do you lie about the food you have eaten (someone else must have eaten it)?

3. Are there certain foods which you cannot give up (this is specially true of chocoholics)?

If this is sounding familiar to you then you should ask yourself whether you could survive 24 hours, two days or a week without any of the foods which you know you eat to excess.

The person who eats compulsively may be driven by either the oral gratification need in themselves, which can be rooted, in a deep need for comfort, or they can be actually "hooked" on some ingredient in the food itself. This is quite common in those people addicted to chocolate. Therefore you need a two-pronged assault on the problem.

Try to identify whether you are driven to eat compulsively by outside events, i.e. stress, boredom, or by feelings inside yourself, i.e. depression, loneliness. At the same time also look at the type of foods which you cannot resist. It will probably, but not always, be a food containing a high degree of sugar. This is because sugar gives us a "high" in our body chemistry, which is fine in emergency situations such as chocolate bars for mountain climbers, but is not suitable for ordinary everyday activities. We can become addicted to sugar in the same way that the smoker becomes addicted to nicotine.

If you think that you are a compulsive eater then at the end of this Chapter when you are playing the tape you should, at the point in the audio where I say "I want you to go back to any part of your body where you can feel any tension" you repeat to yourself

> "In the future I will avoid those foods which I know I am at present addicted to. I will replace them with proper balanced meals, and I will eat only when my stomach tells me I am hungry, NOT for any other reason.
>
> As I begin to control my food addiction I will begin to feel much calmer and relaxed and, as the days go by, my control will become more and more natural to me, until I am eating quite sensibly and healthily again".

Practice the relaxation technique each week until the end of the course and insert the above at the appropriate moment and you will find that you will be able to control your eating and thereby your weight.

The other eating disorders Anorexia Nervosa and Bulimia are an attempt by the individual to exert control over one part of their life, their weight and body image as perceived by themselves.

Anorexia nervosa has the following characteristics

1. It begins prior to the age of 25

2. The behaviour leads to a marked loss of body weights (usually those who are 20% below average body weight for height and build)

3. In women there can be cessation of periods.In both sexes there can be slow pulse rate, vomiting. and excessive fine body hair.

4. There is a distortion in the person's attitude towards food which does not respond to rational argument.

Women tend to be the prime sufferers of anorexia nervosa but men do make up 10% of sufferers.

The reasons put forward for anorexia nervosa are many and varied, but it would appear that whatever the underlying cause of the desire to lose weight, once body weight falls below that which is necessary for normal body functioning, the problem spirals downwards.

Whether it is slimming which has got out of hand, problems related to childhood, current problems in handling adulthood, or depression, once a healthy eating pattern is broken it is compounded by the effects of poor nutrition.

Therefore if you know that you are well below the normal body weight given by the table in this Chapter and you are not suffering or being treated for any other medical problem then you should look very carefully at your eating habits.

If you can answer yes to any of the questions on *page 63* you should seek medical advice or contact the agencies whose names are given at the end of this Chapter. There will be people there who are especially sympathetic to those with eating disorders, particularly anorexia nervosa.

DO YOU

1 Limit your calorific intake to less than 1000 calories a day?

2. Do you eat alone deliberately?

3. Do you hide your body from others, friends, parents etc.?

4. Do you binge occasionally?

5. Can you pass 24 hours without worrying about your weight?

Anorexia bulimia is a secondary stage in anorexia nervosa, which involves the use of laxatives, and self-induced vomiting in order to control body weight. There is also the pattern of uncontrollable bingeing of food.

This pattern can disguise quite successfully the underlying problem since meals are eaten in a normal fashion with the family but are regurgitated later.

This pattern of vomiting and use of laxatives has health risks attached and the practice puts great strain on other areas of the body. Kidney problems, due to an imbalance of potassium and sodium ions in the body, oedema, swelling of tissues in the body, and even epileptic fits can arise from the long-term practice of bulimia.

If you can recognise the bingeing and use of laxatives as the pattern of your means of controlling your weight then you are a sufferer of bulimia nervosa and you should also seek advice from your medical practitioner or from the agencies listed on *page 65*.

EXERCISE ADDICTION

While regular exercise is necessary and healthy like any thing else in life it can be taken to extremes and when it becomes compulsive it is an addiction.

When we exercise we release chemicals called endorphins into the bloodstream which gives us a pleasurable 'high'. In most people this is just a transitory thing but in others they become hooked on the endorphins in the same way that smokers are on nicotine.

Why should this be a problem, since exercise is healthier than smoking?

If a person becomes obsessed with exercising there can be physical problems due to overuse of certain muscle groups and strain and damage can occur. Also psychologically anything which becomes obsessive so that it obliterates all other aspects of life is not advisable.

A good gym will always have properly trained coaches who recognise that this problem with exercise addiction can occur and who know the signs to look for in their clients. Listen to the coach and if he says you should only exercise 3 times a week, do not try to squeeze in extra sessions.

For anyone who recognises that they are addicted to weight control or to exercise the following words should be repeated at the point in the relaxation audio when I say "now go back to any part of your body where you can feel any tension"

I recognise that I am trying to
control my body in a way which
is not natural.
As I listen to the audio I feel this
need for control leaving me
and as this need for control leaves
me I am able to start
eating or exercising in a normal
fashion, and I feel
calmer and more relaxed and
confident about myself.

USEFUL ADDRESSES FOR FURTHER INFORMATION ON EATING DISORDERS

b-eat
103 Prince of Wales Road
Norwich
Norfolk NR1 1DW
www.b-eat.co.uk
Tel: 0845 634 1414 (Helpline)

The National Centre for Eating Disorders
54 New Road
Esher
Surrey KT10 9NU
www.eating-disorders.org.uk
Tel: 0845 838 2040

VISUALISATION NO. 4 - THE WATER GARDEN

You are opening a wrought iron gate into a walled, paved courtyard, in the centre of which
is a large ornate fountain.
It is warm and pleasant in the garden so you sit down in a corner to rest and watch the
water cascading down into the pool at the base of the fountain.

In the centre of the fountain is a marble figure of a woman holding a large fish from
whose mouth the water is spurting.
The sunlight is shining across the stream of water from the fish, dividing into coloured
beams of light and, as the water splashes into the water in the pool, ripples spread out
over the surface.

The garden is quiet except for the splashing of the water in the fountain and the faint
hum of insects buzzing round the brightly coloured flowers set in tubs in each corner of
the courtyard.

In the far corner you see a cat lying in the sunshine, it slowly stretches itself, rearranges
its position and then lies down to doze again.
On the rim of the fountain a bird is balancing while occasionally dipping its beak into the
cool water.

The steady splash, splash of the fountain is very soothing to your ears and the continual
rippling of the water concentrates your attention.
You watch each ripple as it starts from the centre and moves out towards the edge of the
pool to be replaced again and again by another and another.

Perhaps life is like the water, forever flowing but with ripples on the surface breaking up
the flow only to reform again into smoothness,
and as you watch the ever repeating ripples you find that in the warmth and peace of the
garden you too are becoming peaceful and tranquil.

VISUALISATION NO. 4 - THE WATER GARDEN

NOW Read the passage again.

PLAY THE AUDIO

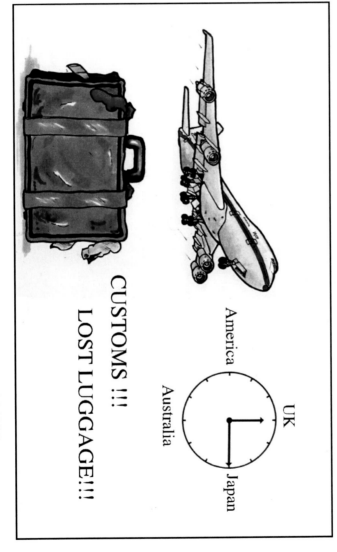

THE STRESS ASSOCIATED WITH BUSINESS TRAVEL

CUSTOMS !!!
LOST LUGGAGE!!!

America

Australia

UK

Japan

CHAPTER V

BUSINESS TRAVEL

As you will see from the picture on *page 68*, this chapter is devoted to the stress associated with business travel and how this can best be minimised.

A good place to start is to ask why should travel on business cause stress, when travelling, especially abroad, is considered by many people to be an added perk of the executive position?

The business executive usually lives at home, goes to work and returns each evening. There is a familiar environment and a regular routine. To break this for a day or two is often stimulating and therefore welcomed but once the absence become regular, say several days, a fortnight, a month or home only for weekends, a different life pattern is imposed.

This new pattern involves the strain of travel, be this by road, rail or air; the bore of living in hotels with only food, drink and television, absence from home, possibly time change, and much higher work load in selling, negotiating, representing etc., away from familiar surroundings, often when feeling, tired, disorientated and lonely. To do this regularly can make a drain on an executive's physical and emotional resources and it is important for the company to monitor the number of trips away each year and conditions under which these are undertaken, to make sure that good employees are not burnt out prematurely.

Travel on business is best categorised under

1. Travel within the U.K.

2. European and short distance travel

3. Worldwide travel against time

TRAVEL IN THE U.K.

Let us first consider then travel in the United Kingdom. The senior executive should make sure that travel is by the most appropriate route. On the whole it is far better that executives go by train or plane rather than driving themselves by car and that they are met and looked after on arrival. Anyone who earns more than £300,000 and who really has to drive more than say, 15,000 miles per year, even from home to work merits a chauffeur.

Recordings of pulse and blood pressures have been made during 4-hour car, plane and train journeys. There is no doubt that more stress, as measured by raised blood pressure and pulse, is produced by car driving than is produced by the other two methods.

Modern technology has produced small electrocardiac recorders, which can be attached to the chest so that the heart's behaviour can be continuously monitored. Such electrocardiograms show dramatic changes during driving, particularly when the subject is caught in a traffic jam or tries to overtake. Subjects with previously normal electrocardiograms will show unhealthy patterns at these times, while those who have previously suffered coronary heart disease will produce very unhealthy patterns under these pressures.

The effect of travelling even within the U.K. is that there is an inevitable tendency to leave earlier and get home later, and there is also the problem of coping with the ordinary work which would have otherwise been done.

EUROPEAN AND SHORT DISTANCE TRAVEL

Now I shall turn to the second category of business travel, which is European and short distance travel. Travel within Europe, usually by air, and by flights of mostly up to three hours and often much shorter duration, presents quite different problems to longer flights eastwards and westwards. European travel crosses fewer time zones and involves minimum time shift. This means that the day is not seriously distorted and that there is only the normal fatigue and anxiety of travel to deal with.

Although not particularly difficult the actual process of short-haul air travel is nothing like as comfortable and convenient as the airlines would have one think. Airports are inconveniently situated, parking is time consuming, planes are late, overcrowding occurs in the lounges and information is not always easily available, plus the extra delays due to security measures. All this, plus the natural anxiety that many feel when travelling, the stress of dealing with foreigners or negotiating in a foreign language plus staying in hotels, equals extra strain for the business man and woman compared with a normal day or week's work in the office.

The best way to reduce fatigue is to stay at central hotels, use taxis or hired cars whenever possible, phone home regularly and above all be home by Friday. With travelling in Europe increasing, there is a growing tendency for the executive's weekend to be eroded away. The company should insist that such people are home by Friday night, and do not leave again until Monday morning. If possible they should be met at the airport and driven home in a company car. Wherever possible first class seats should be booked.

WORLDWIDE TRAVEL

Thirdly we must consider the effects of worldwide travel against time. No sensible company or individual would expect to take major decisions at 3 o'clock in the morning after a long and gruelling day, yet travellers leap off aeroplanes and, because the sun is shining, go enthusiastically if somewhat bemused, into difficult negotiations.

Since travel against time is air travel, compared to a sea journey which gives time for the body to adapt, I have listed below ten various tips for making your journey a more comfortable one.

1. Plan flight well in advance, have a day flight if possible, try to arrive at normal bedtime, and adapt gradually. Let me expand on that last phrase - adapt gradually. Have you ever paused to think why your body works so smoothly and how it is that you wake up, go to sleep, feel hungry and so on at regular and predetermined intervals? Our basic behaviour pattern is determined by a series of conditioned reflexes and finely adjusted responses. Therefore, when the body runs down at the end of the day, the supply of various hormones is reduced, body temperature drops and various other changes associated with sleep and recharging the batteries take place.

    All this is controlled on the basis of an in-built 24 hour biological clock and is called the body's circadian rhythm. It gives all the various systems an in-built time base. If then, you suddenly fly to the West Coast of America with a time change of plus eight hours on a 14 to 15 hour flight, the natural rhythm is turned more or less inside out. Day is turned into night and the body is asked to eat when it should be asleep, be intelligent when it is used to relaxing and so on.

Detailed biochemical and other research has shown that the body takes at least five days to reset its clock after a major shift in time base. Until this has occurred, there is deterioration in performance. To do nothing for five days after arrival is asking too much of most busy people. An appreciable amount of acclimatization does occur however in 24-36 hours, so that if sensible travel rules are observed, a fair compromise can be made. Major time changes occur on east/west flights (when days become longer) and west/east flights when days become shorter. Flying roughly north to south imposes little time change and depending on Summer Time, London to Cape Town causes little biological upset although it is as far away as America.

2.   Lead as quiet as life as possible the 24 hours before the flight. This means avoiding an all-night party with plenty of alcohol just before a flight, when the effects of lack of sleep and drink would be added to the fatigue of travelling.

3.   Stop smoking before and while flying. The effects of smoking are sustained over hours, therefore treat this as in No. 2. The hazards of smoking while flying are these.

Regular smokers develop a blood carbon monoxide level of about 5%. An effect of this is to reduce the blood oxygen level of a smoker on the ground to that of a nonsmoker flying at an altitude of 7,000 feet. Thus a regular smoker who flies will tend to suffer from symptoms of hypoxia, (oxygen starvation) at lower altitudes than a non-smoker. The difference could be critical.

At 20,000 feet the time of useful consciousness without oxygen is ten minutes. But a regular smoker flying at that altitude without oxygen, after a supply failure, for example will have a blood oxygen level equivalent to that at around 27,000 feet, where the time of useful consciousness is between one or two minutes.

4.   Drink little alcohol in flight. The aircraft's pumped in atmosphere is slightly dry. As a result dehydration can occur. Alcohol increases dehydration so avoid it in flight and be particularly abstemious on long flights to hot countries, dehydration is a serious problem in hot climates.

5.   Eat one main meal as near to your usual time as possible. It is easier to adapt better to new routine if you are hungry. Your breakfast in New York will be all the better if you missed supper, and the digestive and bowel system works better too.

6.   Drink plenty of non-alcoholic and non-sparkling fluids during the flight. We have already covered alcohol and dehydration but it is also important to remember that aircraft are pressurized and this can present problems with gassy liquids.

An aircraft cabin is a communal spacesuit; air is pumped in to keep the pressure at the outside equivalent of 8,000 altitude. For technical reasons it is not possible to achieve ground level pressure in the aircraft and this difference can cause discomfort when gases in the body especially in the intestines expand. Carbonated drinks only add to the amount of gas present in the body.

7.   Wear loose fitting comfortable clothes and shoes. If travelling to a tropical climate wear suitable clothing, particularly natural fibres, which allow perspiration to evaporate. Sitting in the same seat on a long flight puts continuous pressure on the veins in the thighs. People with varicose veins are most affected and their feet and ankles may swell slightly. Choose shoes which are broken in and comfortable. Avoid crossing the legs as this can aggravate vein problems and walk and up and down the cabin periodically.

8.   Leave a 24 hour rest period after a 5 hour time change before doing any business transactions. This is to allow for the effects of jet lag. We have already covered the body's response to travel over time zones and on *page 76* you will see that there is a formula which can be used to calculate the number of days rest required to overcome jetlag. If you have a mathematical inclination you might to like to alleviate the boredom of the next flight by working out your own rest period using this formula.

9.   Never attend important business functions or take important decisions after an east/west or west/east flight. Reactions can be slowed for two days following a ten-zone trip westward and for three days after a similar eastward trip. Try therefore to arrive over a weekend when you can and allow for at least 24-48 hours of adjustment before starting your business negotiations on Monday.

10.   Take exercise wherever possible during the flight and at re-fuel stops plus practicing relaxation technique. Exercise will help the body's circulation of the blood and relieve the pressure on the legs through sitting for long periods. It will also allow the stomach and intestines to expand and thereby avoid cramps and constipation. Any opportunity to take in fresh air should be welcomed as this will help to dispel the heavy feeling in the head caused by the dryness of the aircraft.

BULEY'S FORMULA FOR
CALCULATING THE NUMBER OF DAYS OF REST
NEEDED TO OVERCOME JET LAG

$$\frac{T/2 + (Z - 4) + Cd + Ca}{10}$$

Where   T = hours in transit
Z = number of time-zones crossed
(take this as 0 if Z is 4 or less)

Cd and Ca are the departure and arrival co-efficient
listed in the table below

Time of day	Departure Co-efficient	Arrival Co-efficient
0800 - 1159	0 = good	4 = bad
1200 - 1759	1 = fair	2 = fair
1800 - 2159	3 = poor	0 = good
2200 - 0059	4 = bad	1 = fair
0100 - 0759	3 = poor	3 = poor

Example
A traveller leaves Ottawa at 1800 hours localtime (Cd = 3), spends eleven hours travelling, and arrives in Vienna at 10.00 hours (Cd = 4) having crossed six time zones. The number of days rest he needs is:

$$\frac{1^{1}/_{2} + 2 + 3 + 4}{10} = 1.45$$

Rounded up to the nearest half-day = 1.5 days

FEAR OF FLYING

Many people who have to fly for business reasons have a fear of doing so. For some it is a feeling of dread which gradually creeps over them from the time the tickets are booked. With others it is held back until arriving at the airport and checking in. With others it is actually when sitting in the aircraft and fastening the seat belt and for others it is the take-off experience and landing.

Whatever your area of fear, for you, it is disabling and uncomfortable and often embarrassing, particular when seated next to someone who obviously enjoys every moment of their flight! This is when being male is an obvious disadvantage since the stiff upper lip approach prevents many men from admitting to anyone except themselves of their fear.

Obviously the reasons for this fear of flying are many and varied. Some are purely on technical grounds, is the aircraft safe? are the screening facilities for explosive devices good enough? Are the procedures for aircraft control when airborne properly monitored?

These are not groundless fears since no-one would travel in a car, bus or train knowing that it is faulty or that the road or rail system is unsafe. However statistics do bear out that flying is 25 times safer than by car.

If your fear is grounded in a rational fear of aircraft safety why not face this fear directly and visit your nearest airport, see if you can arrange to speak to a representative of the airline about their safety record. Most airlines are only too pleased to talk to their customers and to explain the various procedures which must be carried out to ensure safety for all, including the airline staff themselves. If you can visit the airport, walk around knowing that you are not actually going to fly and learn to relax in the terminal this will be the first stage in reducing your tension about flying.

THE AIRPORT

If your fear is based on claustrophobia, which is a common fear affecting many people, whether in lifts, or any confined space, then you need to spend time practising the relaxation technique prior to your next flight. This will also be relevant for people with a fear of heights.

The trouble with any phobia (fear) is that the anticipatory aspect of the fear is sometimes more disabling than the actual event itself. If we have time before the actual event takes place (the flight) we use that time to build up a level of tension about the flight. This means that by the time we are actually on the aircraft we have our bodies in such a state of arousal (the adrenal glands mentioned in Chapter I are operating) that it will take quite some hours for our bodies to return to normal. Therefore we will experience the flight in a state of anxiety which in turn reinforces our perception of flying as an unpleasant experience.

Since those aspects of travel which affect everyone adversely i.e. crowding, heat, noise and fatigue will also be affecting the traveller who has the additional fear of flying, he or she has a much greater need to practise the relaxation technique in order to bring down their arousal level.

Therefore I suggest that before the next flight is booked you continue with your breathing exercises as described in the earlier chapters. When on the aircraft and particularly at the point of take-off you should concentrate on nothing else but your breathing and you should continue to concentrate on your breathing until the aircraft has levelled out.

Also at the point in the audio where I say "in a few moments time I want you to go back to any part of your body where you can feel any tension" I would like you to say to yourself:

> *"whenever I am flying I will be able*
> *to recreate this feeling of relaxation*
> *I have now and as I breathe deeply*
> *and calmly I will be able to relax and*
> *enjoy the flight like other people."*

EFFECTS OF BUSINESS TRAVEL ON THE FAMILY

So far we have discussed the effect of travel on the executive but I feel that we should remember that it can affect other members of the family, particularly the spouse.

The wife who is left alone with only the company of young children is particularly vulnerable as she may well find it difficult to arrange for help with the children so that she can get a break occasionally and she may also be physically isolated and this can pose practical problems especially in the winter months. This is where the company has a responsibility to keep in touch so that if there are crises while the husband is away help can be readily available.

Husbands (and wives) who are abroad for the company should be allowed to phone home frequently at the company's expense, since this will help to bridge the distance far better than letters, which invariably arrive after the sender has returned home.

If the children are older and can be left then it is a nice gesture for the company to allow a wife to accompany her husband on a trip at least once a year or alternatively to meet the husband at a Mediterranean resort on the return journey to have a few days holiday.

With the increase in divorce in the U.K. and the States, which is an additional stress, it seems that companies have some responsibility in allowing couple to make up for the time spent apart rather than forcing them into living entirely separate lives.

The children also miss father (or mother) when they are away and this can show itself in problems during adolescence if not handled carefully.

THE EFFECTS OF TRAUMA WHILST TRAVELLING AND WORKING

This is another subject which has become relevant during the last few years, particularly with the increase in terrorist attacks on commercial buildings and public transport.

Everyone who has to travel in and out of commercial centres for their work is well aware of the dangers posed by the threat of terrorism. However most people are able to continue to travel and work whilst mindful of the various procedures and warnings given by the authorities for dealing with public safety.

But despite all the precautions taken by government, police, and anti-terrorist operations, there are still tragic incidents where people are killed or injured. When this occurs the emergency services come into operation and hospitals cope with the consequences.

Physical injuries are dealt with but often it is the shock factor in such cases which is the most debilitating and which can be manifested many weeks, months or even years after the event, which caused it. It is this reaction of the body to trauma after the event, which has been termed Post Traumatic Stress. It can affect people who are actually injured and also those who witnessed trauma, and it is as distressing and as painful to those suffering it as physical pain and injury.

It is important therefore if anyone has been involved in such a trauma whether as a victim or helper or just a witness and they experience the following symptoms, which do not fade with time, that they seek medical and psychological counselling.

1. There has been an actual event in which they were involved, accident, bomb scare, explosion.
2. They experience the physical symptoms of stress outlined in Chapter I.
3. They have recurrent nightmares or flash backs (relive the experience while awake during the day).
4. Avoidance of places, situations related to the trauma.

Ask about counselling and self-help groups in your area.

VISUALISATION NO. 5 - HEAD AND BODY MASSAGE

Starting with the scalp imagine gentle fingers slowly rotating on your head, moving round and round rhythmically, allowing the tension in your scalp to be released.

Now think of those same fingers moving down the sides of your face, to the temple area where there is a lot of tension and imagine how pleasant and effective a gentle massage there is for tired eyes or the beginnings of a headache.

Having removed the tension from the eye area imagine those fingers moving to the nape of your neck, that area of tension which anyone who works long hours at a desk or driving in heavy traffic can experience.
Think how the gentle but firm pressure of the fingers can find those tense little knots in the back of the neck and can dissolve gradually the pain and discomfort there.

Now moving down to the back and the shoulder region imagine these hands now making long slow strokes from the spine outward and upward towards the shoulder joints and then down across the arms.

Those warm hands increase slightly the pressure and consequently the tension in the shoulders and upper back begins to be released.

Using the same pressure the hands now move downwards across the lower back and over the buttocks which can also become very tense as a result of sitting for long periods. The blood vessels respond to the friction caused on the skin and sensation and warmth returns to tired muscles.

Similarly as the hands move down the upper thighs towards the calves, these too respond by relaxing under the soothing but gentle pressure, and by the end of the session when the feet and hands have been massaged, the body is warm and relaxed when muscle tension has been removed but alive and tingling where the nerve endings of the skin have been stimulated by the increased blood flow at the surface.

VISUALISATION NO. 5 - HEAD AND BODY MASSAGE

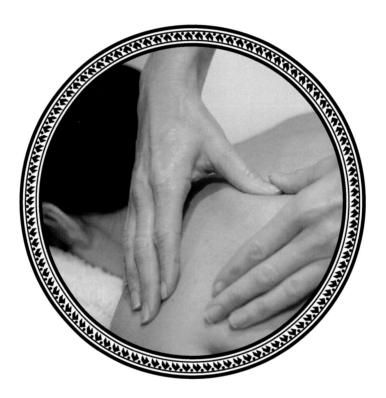

NOW Read the passage again.

PLAY THE AUDIO

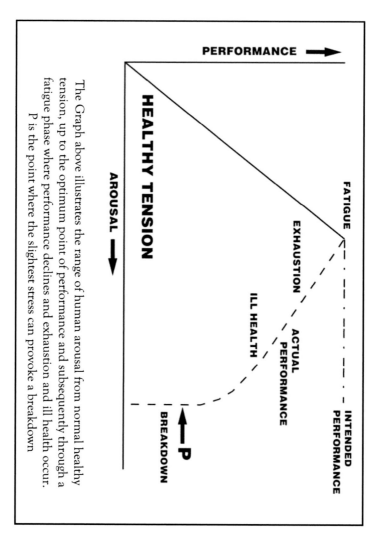

Fig. 7.- THE HUMAN FUNCTION CURVE

The Graph above illustrates the range of human arousal from normal healthy tension, up to the optimum point of performance and subsequently through a fatigue phase where performance declines and exhaustion and ill health occur.

P is the point where the slightest stress can provoke a breakdown

CHAPTER VI

WORK PERFORMANCE

In this chapter I wish to talk specifically about how our work performance can be negatively affected by stress and to explain in greater detail the way in which relaxation therapy enables us to actually improve our energy levels and output of work.

If you look at *page 84* "the Human Function Curve", you will see that once normal healthy tension reaches a certain fatigue point, performance drops away rapidly and exhaustion takes over. The dotted line is the intended level of performance which the individual sets himself - the output to be achieved - the deadlines to be met. If he or she is not slowed down at this point they will inevitably be depleting their energy reserves until these too are gone and ill health occurs.

It is a common phenomenon that people who are in this position often do not realise how hard they are pushing themselves, despite of what family and colleagues say, because of the effects of the surge of adrenalin which is being released. Nevertheless eventually a point P on the diagram is reached and a breakdown occurs.

A good example comes to mind of a Divisional Manager of a well known oil company who, despite working longer and longer hours, ignored the advice of colleagues to slow down because he felt fine. This same man when then sent for a routine medical check up by the Company doctor wasn't even allowed to get up from his seat until he had been given medication because his blood pressure was so high. He was then instructed to take a period of rest and when he did return to work he had to take part in compulsory gym sessions and was eventually retired in his mid fifties, yet until he saw the doctor he was not aware of being over stretched.

This state of being unaware of fatigue can be useful in certain circumstances, fighting soldiers often have to live off adrenalin for short periods when under shell fire but when it is a prolonged and permanent state of arousal it can have fatal consequences.

What conditions can cause us to become so stressed at work that both our bodies and our work performance become affected? Below I have listed the Sources of Work Stress.

SOURCES OF WORK STRESS

1. **Stresses intrinsic to the job**
   Too much/too little work
   Poor physical conditions
   Time pressures

2. **Career development**
   Over-promotion
   Under-promotion
   Lack of job security
   Fear of redundancy
   Thwarted ambition

3. **Role in organisation**
   Role conflict/ambiguity
   Responsibility for people
   No participation in decision making

4. **Relations within the organisation**
   Poor relations with superiors
   Poor relations with colleagues and subordinates

5. **The Individual's personality**
   Tolerance level
   Ability to cope with change
   Motivation

Let us look at each of these sources of work stress in turn.

1. Stresses intrinsic to the job

    a)   Too much work

How much is too much? This will depend of course on the type of work done. Some work is highly paced i.e. telephone calls which are continuously demanding attention and from which there is no escape can be extremely exhausting. So is any work by which the pace is set by a machine, where the machine functions more quickly than man. It is possible to do highly paced work for short periods accurately and with properly spaced breaks, it is when the work period is continuous that the stress builds up and performance suffers. Of course some people find that they operate better at some tasks than others and usually within an office environment natural ability should help with delegation of routine tasks.

Stress and mental tasks

What exactly does "stress" mean? In mechanics it means to place under pressure and to strain until the breaking or fatigue point is reached, and there is usually a simple link between cause and effect. However, when we apply this definition to the human body the subject becomes more complex since both physical and mental factors have to be considered.

Traditionally the approach of the Human Factors Engineer has been to look at the end result - work performance - to gauge the effects of stress on employees - and environmental needs such as temperature, noise levels and adequate work breaks have been emphasised. In recent years however there has been a shift in emphasis towards the individual employee rather than the working environment, and, although such needs are still relevant when looking at work performance at higher levels, supervisory, management and Board status, the importance of mental factors over physical factors becomes evident.

b) Too little work

An important factor in stress levels is boredom. Boredom is described by various sources as a subjectively unstimulating condition resulting in feelings of apathy, or a state of satiation where the person has "had enough" of a particular activity. The physiology of boredom is more precisely described as a result of a decline in stimuli and therefore the functional state of the body is also reduced.

Some working environments promote boredom, i.e. where training is inadequate, there is little opportunity for physical movement, poor lighting and overheated offices and working alone. The personal factors related to boredom are fatigue shift workers who have not adapted, low motivation, work which is beneath the education level and ability of the person and work which is unchallenging.

c) Time Pressures

In an organisation where there are formal job descriptions and employee appraisal procedures, employees will be assigned to positions which match their intellectual capacity. However, even where there is such perfect matching, performance can be adversely affected by TIME PRESSURE and researchers have shown that when decision making is carried out under time pressure conditions, the stress factor can be measured using heart rate readings taken at the beginning, the end and after the decision making process has been completed.

During the actual time when the decision is being made the subjects under time pressure do not show much greater stress levels than subjects without the time pressure, but it is in the post-decision phase that a real difference in stress is recorded. Management is fundamentally concerned with making decisions and it follows that, when there is a constant state of work overload and pressure of time, the stress levels will become permanently raised.

Time pressures of course vary from one business to another. Accountants are typically more hard pressed at the end of the financial year and marketing executives at the time of a new product launch. I am sure you have your own busy period.

2. Career Development

Over promotion: This may seem to be unlikely to many people, particularly those who feel that it is more often the case that people wait in vain for promotion that never comes.

However in some industries and in particular circumstances it is possible for an individual with special abilities to be promoted over his or her peers into a high powered position.

For example a young computer specialist who is exceptionally talented and at the forefront of their field is given special status by the company board who see their talents as extending profits and also placing the company ahead in the market place before the competition. Fine you may say, where is the problem with that?

Depending on the personality and background of the individual concerned, asking someone in their 20's to be at the same level of management as those in their 40's and 50's in a large company where status and hierarchy are strictly adhered to, can foster resentment and bitterness. Also if the individual given the promotion is also expected to socialise at the same level as those twenty years their senior, unless they come from a background and culture that makes the transition easy, it can be more stressful attending a management cocktail party than actually working at the job itself.

Underpromotion: This is an area which, I think many people can identify with. Most people at one time or another feel that their particular talents and abilities are not being fully appreciated. Under promotion is a very definite source of stress and this is linked with thwarted ambition. Obviously the more dynamic personality will be more frustrated if unable to realise his or her potential.

There are always times at work when we feel undervalued, want a pay rise and our colleagues appear to be geting more out of the company than we are. But a distinction must be drawn between those feelings which come as a result of tiredness, need for a holiday and problems outside work and those of justifiable frustration. If you are constantly dealing with a deep nagging feeling of underachievement what should you do about it?

First of all is there any chance of change in the near future, a departmental or personal appraisal, or a change in the company structure that will work to your advantage? Are you waiting for someone to retire, this is not such a likely option nowadays as reaching retirement age in a company is not such a sure thing as twenty years ago.

If the change you need is not in the foreseeable future, should you force the pace yourself? This depends on individual circumstances. Is the company viable, are they making profits? In some cases poor profitability has the effect of freezing all staff movement in a company, other than that of shedding unnecessary labour. Also it can mean less or no overtime and a pay freeze and/ or reduced working hours.

Can you make out a good case for your promotion, will it bring benefits to he company as well as for yourself? What are you really seeking - more interesting and challenging work even at the same salary or more status and an increase in pay and perks? It is important to be clear in your own mind about this, as simply complaining about differentials to the Personnel Department will not usually bring forth an enthusiastic response.

If, at the end of the day, you feel that the chances of being promoted within your existing company have been explored and rejected, there is the option of staying put and living with the situation or changing to another company. Action at this point will depend on how much of a risk taker you are and how good or bad the employment market is that time for your particular talents. Sometimes moving into temporary contract work bridges the gap, it allows for a break in work pattern without the accompanying financial risk.

Lack of job security and fear of redundancy: This is an area which, has become more and more relevant since I first started my courses. Job security affects everyone and for those with dependants and mortgages and other fixed outgoings the fear of losing one's job is a major one.

Unfortunately because of the effects of the recession in the late 80's and early 90's the way in which employers approach employees has changed. Insecurity has occurred on both sides of the employment divide and as a result there are fewer long term career type positions being offered and more short term contracts, which pay reasonably well, but do not hold out long term security. Even those traditionally 'safe' employers, the Banks, have been shedding labour to an extent which could not have been envisaged 15 years ago.

The effects on people of this change in employment practice depends on their age. Those who grew up and were educated and employed back in the sixties and seventies had a pattern of working life before them in which change had no real part. Personal life might change marriage, children etc but working life was set early on.

This has been completely altered and those who have come on to the employment scene since the 80's and 90's have entered a world where change is a pre-requisite of working life, adaptability is the way to survive and constant retraining and updating of skills to keep pace with technology a necessity. The rules of Darwin's Natural Selection now apply in the employment field and it has left a legacy of men and women whose working lives have been curtailed or altered beyond recognition as the unemployment figures show.

But this does not mean that redundancy, early retirement or simply being 'let go' with or without a golden handshake is the end of the world. It is a question of attitude, is the bottle half full or half empty? and many people have discovered unused skills and different talents because of a change in circumstances. This will be explored more fully in Chapter IX.

3. Role in the Organisation

To be happy and contented in his/her work a person must know what the job actually entails and what their role is in the organisation. Uncertainty is one of the main causes of stress.

In an ideal world a job description accompanies every new employee together with a written outline or chart of lines of authority and responsibility within the company. The larger the company the more likely this is to occur, since large companies would be unable to function as the numbers of employees and breakdown of divisions, departments and management layers would become unfathomable without a 'corporate map'.

It is the small to medium sized company where life is more on an "ad hoc" basis that problems of individual roles can arise. People are often taken on initially in one role, are moved to another department and acquire another role, two departments are merged and two jobs also made into one, someone retires or leaves and their work is passed over or shared out amongst others and new technology is introduced and a completely new role is created overnight, with or without the necessary training.

These are the areas where friction can occur, when an offer to help out short term turns to custom and practice but without the official recognition or increase in pay and status. Also where no one is quite sure who is accountable to whom and there is a tendency for no-one to be accountable for anything!

Another area of stress is where incompatible demands are made and this is usually the middle manager's domain, with Board policy making and budgeting being met by demands for increases in personnel, equipment, manhours, administrative functions and trade union legislation coming up from below.

Responsibility for people: there are those roles at work in which a person is made to be responsible for others' work performance e.g. a supervisor, departmental head, tutor, team leader. This responsibility can be stressful since taking responsibility for one's own work is often considered enough in life without having to watch the performance of others and correct them. But this is an essential part of the transition from the managed to manager and it has to be faced and dealt with.

People who are supervised, managed etc. are just the same as those who do the supervising and managing. They are individuals and with all the characteristic traits and mannerisms that endear or repel according to our own personalities. But regardless of whether they are liked or loathed they have to be managed!

It is therefore in everyone's interests to retain what is best described as a fair, relaxed and firm manner without prejudice or bias if one to one communication is to be maintained. Creating unnecessary friction in an office or any commercial environment is just bad management practice.

Where the responsibility for people is total i.e. the Personnel Department, then the stress factor is built in as part of the job. An engineer can mend or send for another component if it fails on a job, it is not so easy when you are dealing with human beings. If you are in personnel work you have to like people, unless you are a masochist, since you will be dealing with people problems everyday. This has been traditionally a female role, probably because men saw it as one with a lot of stress attached and decided "women were better at dealing with people problems". Recently with the increase in the computerisation of payroll, performance related pay and other financial incentives, the Personnel Manager's role has been raised in status.

People are more likely to back a proposal to which they have contributed and if their contribution is given recognition they will be quite likely to persuade others of its benefit too.

4. Relations within the Organisation

Poor relations with superiors: This can occur when an individual has had inadequate training and therefore cannot fulfil the expectations of those who are responsible for his/her work performance.

It can also occur where there are poor methods of communication (too many memos and not enough face to face meetings). Sometimes it is because communication is one way only downwards. People should be encouraged to ask for help, give suggestions and generally have some input into the work process.

Poor relations with colleagues and subordinates: Once again communication is the key. Resentment, irritation, misunderstandings etc. are usually the result of A not knowing how to speak to B.

Some people communicate very well by telephone, where no eye contact is involved, others prefer the written word - memos pour forth daily! Others prefer to have face to face meetings. The latter are often far more effective in handling mis-understandings but not everyone has those natural "dealing with people" skills.

Many companies now run internal communication skill courses, with role play and teamwork practice, which is supervised by an outside consultant in Human Behaviour Skills. Such courses can be very effective in breaking down the prejudices and shyness of people and encouraging them to present themselves in a more positive fashion to others.

Difficulty in delegating responsibility: Delegation is the key to good management and also to relieving stress from overwork.

People who have difficulty in delegating make life difficult for others around them, since they become like magpies, hoarding information and preventing the smooth flow of communication from one department to another. Admittedly with the arrival of computer technology, much essential information is available now on line but there will always be those who see secrecy as a power base.

Delegation is not however about losing power but rather of retaining it. It is a matter of delegating the right things to the right people and this is where management expertise is involved. A senior executive should be spending at least 90% of his/her time managing others and only a small proportion of the remaining 10% doing things himself. Obviously farther down the management line the ratio between doing and managing will decrease.

Delegation should always be to an INDIVIDUAL -as an individual can be held accountable. If you try to delegate to a group - accountability can become difficult.

Be sure exactly what is it you are delegating - make sure the terms of reference are exact and also that the person to whom you are delegating is capable of carrying out the task. The buck will come back to you eventually, so this is a priority.

Make sure that the AUTHORITY to do the task is established. You will naturally have the authority for some tasks, those to whom you delegate will need to receive this authority for others co-operation.

Remember to give PRAISE AND RECOGNITION when a delegated job has been done well, and above all do not feel threatened by others success. This merely means that you have more time and energy to devote to getting your own goals within the company realised.

5. The Individual's Personality

Tolerance level: Because personality is as important as ability where management skills are concerned, researchers have carried out studies on groups of business executives and discovered that they are broadly broken down into two groups Type A and Type B.

Type A characteristics are summarised on *page 97* and broadly these men create deadlines if none exist and become obsessed with number and quantities rather than quality as a measure of success.

Many have an aggressive drive which, borders on habitual hostility. See *page 98*. They generally have few hobbies outside their work and feel guilty when ever they try to relax and work is on their minds even on holiday. They also tend to abuse their bodies with too much rich food, they smoke and drink more than average and, except for an occasional hard fought game of squash or tennis, they consider regular exercise a waste of time.

THE TYPE 'A' PERSONALITY

CHARACTERISTICS   Positive

1. High achievement

2. Self-motivated

3. Hard driving competitiveness

4. Self-imposed deadlines - harrying sense of urgency

5. Tend to occur in professional/technical/ managerial persons aged between 36 - 55 years of age

CHARACTERISTICS   Negative

6. Unwilling to delegate

7. Eat and drink on the job

8. Unable or unwilling to re-schedule work to an eight hour working day

9. Suppresses fatigue symptoms

10. Symptoms of behaviour pattern include coronary heart disease, high blood pressure, increased blood cholesterol levels, lack of exercise, increased smoking and drinking and poor family relations

THE 'A' TYPE PERSONALITY

The findings of a study of 3,500 men over ten years showed the Type A men were almost 3 times as likely to get coronary heart disease than Type B.

Type B personalities are placid, long suffering, rarely moved to anger and, needless to say, far more easy to live and work with. They carry out their tasks in life with equanimity and manage to balance demands of home and work and social life far better than Type A.

WHICH TYPE DO YOU THINK YOU ARE?

Ability to cope with life change:

Change is inevitable. We are changing from the minute we are born and so are those around us. The society in which we live changes also, slowly sometimes but also suddenly such as when new advances in technology change our work and leisure activities.

It is natural for us to cling on to that which is familiar, after all good health, friends, neighbours, a career, and home and family and possessions are the things which help to define us. The younger person has usually more of a sense of adventure and seeks change for its own sake but as we grow older for many of us, what is familiar and safe is what we hold on to.

At home and in our personal life this may not pose a problem but at work, particularly those whose activities are in areas where there is fast and dramatic change, the effects can be devastating. Information technology for example is now taken for granted by today's school leavers but was unknown by their grandparents. In one lifetime mass communication has grown to a point which could not be envisaged 50 years ago.

If change is inevitable how do we cope? By constantly adjusting and with flexibility the survival of the species is based upon adaption and this is never more true than in the workplace. However, adaptation is easier if an open attitude to learning has been retained. A blinkered "it's always been done this way" approach will result in individuals being bypassed or seen as a hindrance to modernising a company's methods.

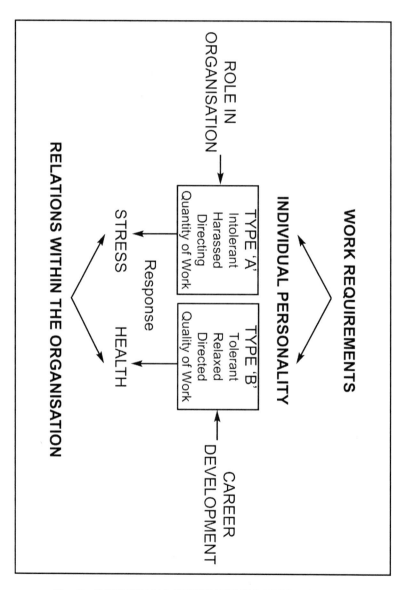

Fig. 8. - INDIVIDUAL RESPONSE TO WORK STRESS

Motivation: Motivation is a factor which has both interested and vexed psychologists and human relations specialists since the turn of the century. A variety of theories have been advanced during that time as to what actually motivates people to work well and consistently.

It has been suggested that people work primarily to keep themselves and their families fed and housed, and this is still a most basic need. However in the Welfare State where these basic needs can be fulfilled (even if not satisfactorily) there is still a need within those un-employed to return to work. This is based on the individual's need for self-esteem and companionship as well as more material benefits.

At work, what motivates one person to work well at a task rather than his or her colleague or to be more ambitious than another? In the first instance getting the right person in the right job is essential. Sometime people will work well for short periods even in jobs they dislike if, either they are very well paid, or they know it is for a limited time. However, coming in day after day to a job which is either boring, too difficult, or which just does not use your abilities is guaranteed to promote stress or disinterest.

Ambition is correlated more with personality. It is an unfortunate fact of life that those who are talented and conscientious do not always climb the ladder to success. Personal drive and ambition and a degree of ruthless self-interest is often a motivating factor and it is this which differentiates those who lead and those who are led.

But often those who are successful in monetary terms pay the price in their personal life and health, whereas the more contented worker may not achieve fame and fortune but is more likely to survive to enjoy his or her retirement.

On *page 100* there is a diagram, which shows how all, these work pressures interrelate with the individual.

On *page 102* I have given you another Visualisation to assist with the relaxation audio. By now you should be finding the breathing technique and muscle relaxation becoming a natural process and I will explain in Chapter VII how the production of Alpha waves in our brains while listening to the audio helps us to relax both mind and body.

VISUALISATION NO. 6 - STILLNESS

Imagine you are far out in space with no noise and with no light
save that from the stars and reflected light from the moon
and the earth.

It is very black and there is no wind and the only sound
you can hear is your own breathing.

As you listen to your breathing you find that you are letting go
of all the thoughts and anxieties
that crowd into your mind and as these thoughts and anxieties
leave you, your mind can simply be -
no thinking - just a resting state -
suspended between activity and sleep -
and while this resting state is happening to you,
you are able to look down below and see the earth slowly revolving,
semi-illuminated in a black void.

You can see the different continents -
Africa, Asia, North and South America, Europe and
Australia and the north and south poles.
How small they seem at these distances - yet how familiar.
All that life which is teeming upon the earth's surface is
unseen from this distance, yet you know it exists.

This quality of timelessness and stillness from the earth
fills your whole being and you feel as if you
and it are become one.
You let the stillness enter every part of your body and
as it pervades your being you find you are drawing strength and
calmness from this stillness.

VISUALISATION NO. 6 - STILLNESS

NOW Read the passage again.

PLAY THE AUDIO

CHAPTER VII

RELAXATION AND BIOFEEDBACK

Now that you have had six weeks experience of the technique of deep relaxation, I have set out below the changes which will have occurred during your relaxation sessions.

Body changes during deep relaxation

If practised correctly, deep relaxation should result in a marked decrease in the body's oxygen consumption. The other condition, in which this occurs is in sleep and hibernation, this has been documented by electroencephalograph studies.

There is an increase in alpha (brain) waves in relaxation, which are not found in sleep. The alpha waves occur during periods of relaxed wakefulness.

There may also be some sensation of change in body temperature - either warmer or cooler - depending on your powers of visualisation.

The heart rate should decrease and muscle tension lessen.

You will have felt for yourself how this ability to relax deeply is helping you day by day and in this Chapter, I will be explaining how the process works and how it has been monitored, using biofeedback technology. But first let me say a little about the terms FEEDBACK and BIOFEEDBACK.

FEEDBACK

"Feedback" means exactly that - to feed back to the originator of an action the response generated by that action and this can be applied to both human action or system response in engineering terms.

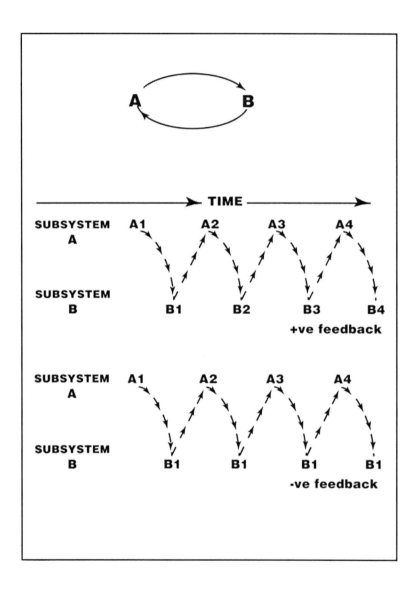

Fig. 9. - THE FEEDBACK LOOP

Feedback is a natural phenomenon. It is a safety device in practical application and it also allows for progress by trial and error. It is accepted and promoted by scientists and engineers as part of "systems" knowledge and by educational psychologists and teachers as a necessary factor in the learning process. It is built into our physiology to maintain homeostasis (balance) - and is present from birth. Developmental psychologists maintain that babies need to have feedback from their mothers (or mother substitute) for normal development.

Systems engineers see feedback as a control element, either as negative feedback, preventing environmental disturbances affecting the output of the system or positive, where there is an intention to alter the output. Both these concepts can be applied to the feedback system of the human body.

It is important to remember that feedback is not moving backwards against time and time is always moving forwards The feedback loop is a conceptual way of looking at a repetitious sequence of events and is the link between the first state and the final state in a phase cycle *(see page 106)*

If we move away from engineering systems into that of the human system we have to accept that human behaviour is extremely complex and can be controlled by some external forces and yet resist control by others. Human beings also vary in their culture and education so that they will have differing responses to outside controls and also the internal environment, which includes that control of one subsystem of the nervous system by another.

BIOFEEDBACK AND THE HUMAN NERVOUS SYSTEM

In order to understand how biofeedback works it is helpful to have a basic knowledge of the nervous system of the human body.

The human nervous system is the structure which, together with the endocrine system, perceives any change in either the external environment (the outside world), the internal environment (the conditions inside our body) and the inter-cellular environment (the condition within individual cells).

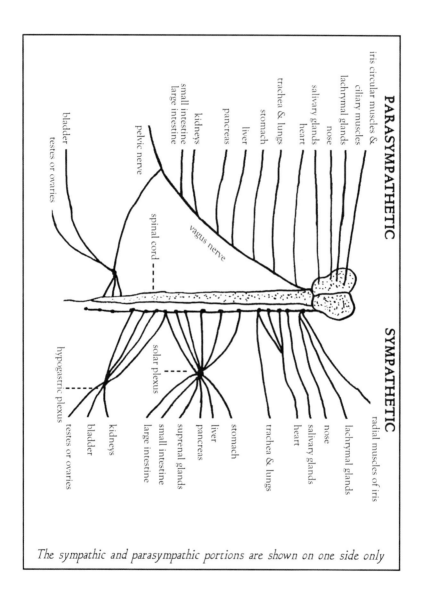

The sympathic and parasympathic portions are shown on one side only

Fig. 10. - THE MAIN NERVES OF THE AUTONOMIC SYSTEM

The nervous system has three main sections,

> The Central Nervous System -brain and spinal cord
>
> The Nerves
>
> The Sense Organs

The sense organs are stimulated by changes in the environment, which send nerve impulses along the afferent nerves to the central nervous system and this in turn sends nerve impulses back along the efferent nerves to the muscles or glands.

As you will already be aware, we have five major sense organs, the eyes, the nose, the ears, the tongue and the skin, and, in addition, we have balance and position receptors in the ears. The five senses of sight, hearing, touch, smell and taste we are familiar with but there are also many, many other sense receptors in all parts of the body of which we are never aware until something amiss occurs.

NEURONS

These are the millions of cells which, make up the central nervous system. Each neurone has a cell body, with a nucleus, and in order to communicate with other cells there are protuberances called dendrites, which convey impulses into the cell and one long protuberance called an axon, which conveys impulses out of the cell. The spaces between neurones form a network of junctions called synapses and the nerve impulses pass across the synapses when a) there is sufficient strength of impulses and b) there are sufficient number of synaptic junctions receiving the impulses.

Nerve and muscle cells give off an electrical discharge caused by the change in polarisation of ions in the cell chemistry and the energy dissipated in active contraction is renewed almost as quickly as it is used. This gives a second charge in the electrical activity of the cells which signals its build up of energy back to "resting" levels. This discharge and recovery of the electrical energy is relatively large for any one cell and is detected by suitable electronic instruments. A code is used by neurones, which is dependent on the number of nerve impulses conducted along nerve fibres. The muscle cells read the code rhythm.

BIOFEEDBACK TECHNOLOGY IN PRACTICE

THE AUTONOMIC NERVOUS SYSTEM

The nervous system has, in addition to the brain and spinal cord (the central nervous system), an autonomic nervous system which is made up of interconnected nerve cell groups called ganglia and these automatically adjust the body state to changing conditions.

On *page 108* the ganglia are shown on one side and the division of the ganglia into sympathetic and parasympathetic is also shown. Each division has an opposite effect to the other. i.e. the parasympathetic nerve impulses slow the heart beat down and the sympathetic nerve impulses accelerate it. All activity is below the level of consciousness in the autonomic nervous system whereas in the central nervous system there is a degree of conscious control.

BIOFEEDBACK

Let me give you a definition of biofeedback. The best scientific definition I have come across is "the process or technique for learning voluntary control over automatically regulated bodily functions". The term was originally conceived as a short way of describing the process of "feeding back" information to the individual about his/her body's response.

Technology
Biofeedback technology is basically one which uses an instrument to sense by electrodes or transducers, signals of body functions, heart rate, blood pressure, muscle tension and brain waves. This information is amplified and activates a display or auditory tone. The process is a bit like feeling the pulse or taking the blood pressure or temperature, where the information is sensed and is translated as beats per minute, or millimetres of mercury of blood pressure or degrees centigrade or Fahrenheit of temperature.

On *page 110* you can see some biofeedback technology in use. The equipment consists of galvanic skin resistance monitors which record minute electrical changes in the resistance in the sweat in the fingertips. These GSR monitors produce an auditory tone, which is adjusted for private listening so that others in the room are not disturbed by the tone

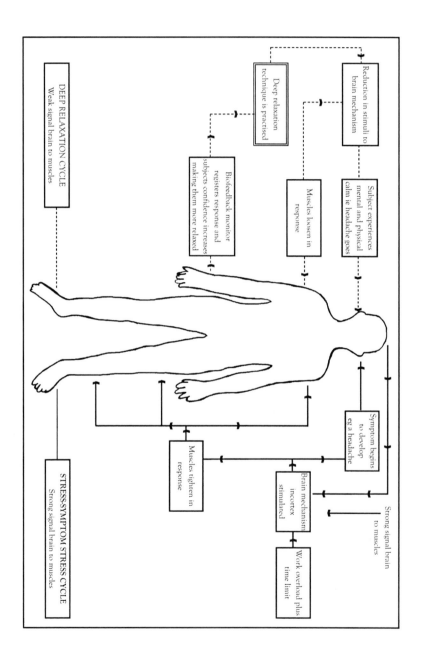

Fig. 11. - CENTRAL NERVOUS SYSTEM MECHANISM & BIO-FEEDBACK

A heart rate monitor can also be used for biofeedback purposes and this has a visual needle display.

Other examples of biofeedback equipment are circles of paper which change colour according to your stress levels (reacting with the chemicals in your skin) and many sport facilities have biofeedback technology to act as safety devices to assess the individual's ability and to avoid injury.

PRACTICAL USES OF BIOFEEDBACK

A. Muscle Training.
Biofeedback has been successfully used in helping thalidomide victims learn to control muscles in the portion of limbs remaining, also with stroke patients and treatment of muscle facial tics. It has also been used to decrease gastric acid secretion in peptic ulcer patients and in heart disease and hypertension.

B. Modification and control of brain waves. *(see page 112)*

BIOFEEDBACK AND RELAXATION

If you look at the diagram on *page 112* this shows in simple form the connection between stress and muscle tension.

When we are under pressure, trying to meet a deadline for example, our brain tells us that we have to accomplish X number of tasks in a restricted time span. This information is passed to our muscles, which results in them contracting with tension.

As time passes, and perhaps we are not keeping up with the workload as planned, then an extra stimulus is sent to the muscles and even more tension results. We will now be aware of a headache developing, or that our lower back hurts or that a migraine is coming on.

We are now in a vicious circle of stress - symptom - stress and we have to find a way of breaking this circle and reversing the information coming to the muscles from our brain. The pathway from the brain is very strong for good reason. It is this pathway which causes our hand to jerk back quickly when we touch a very hot surface. In fact it is a reflex which occurs without us consciously being aware of it.

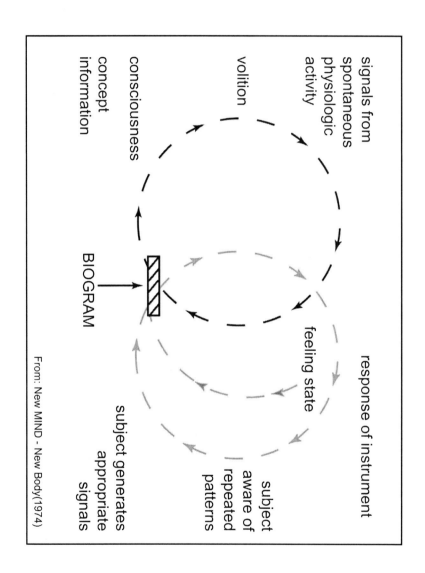

signals from
spontaneous
physiologic
activity

volition

consciousness

concept
information

BIOGRAM

response of instrument

feeling state

subject
aware of
repeated
patterns

subject generates
appropriate
signals

From: New MIND - New Body(1974)

Fig. 12. - A BIOGRAM

When the messages from the brain are affecting muscles causing us pain, we should not try to carry on but we should rather put the system into reverse by practising deep relaxation. This will result in fewer impulses being sent via the efferent nerves to the muscles.

Why should you use deep relaxation technique in addition to stopping work? Spontaneous relaxation following increased tension occurs very slowly. Even deep sleep is not the answer, since subconscious memories can keep the muscles tenses during sleep and dreaming may actually increase the tension further. Since tension diminishes slowly it can still be at a high level when another tension producing situation occurs.

If these events are frequent or if we continue to mull over things again and again, two muscle events occur. Muscle tension becomes sustained at a higher level and may continue to increase and the tightness of the muscles causes them to be hyperactive. You have probably noticed how uptight and tense people startle easily and vigorously. The biofeedback technology shown on the diagram is a useful aid to those who are sceptical about the effectiveness of deep relaxation and for those who find that the feedback given by the technology helps them, but it is by no means a necessity.

BRAIN ACTIVITY - ALPHA WAVES

Biofeedback is not confined to muscle activity alone but involves electrical activity in the brain also. Brain waves are the product of electrochemical interactions in brain cells. When these cells, which have the function of assembling and transmitting information throughout the body, by firing in unison, rhythmic impulses can be detected on the surface of the scalp. Between 8-13 cycles per second are the alpha waves, 14 cycles per second and over are the beta waves, between four to seven cycles per second are the theta waves and between 0.5 to 6 cycles are the delta waves.

Although there is usually more than one frequency operating at any one time, each frequency has its own "mood" characteristic:-

> Alpha - mental and physical relaxation
>
> Beta - alertness, arousal reaction
>
> Theta - replace alpha waves during sleep
>
> Delta - present only during sleep

Can brain waves be brought under conscious control? Yes, although it needs some practice.

In the eastern cultures the practice of meditation and mental self awareness is assimilated into the everyday approach to life but in the West our culture does not lead us to develop the sensitivity to detect subtle shifts in our emotional chemistry. To feel means to be aware, but we learn to feel by using stimulants such as television, drugs, alcohol and loud music, which actually reduces the ability to feel.

A researcher in 1968 found alpha incidentally whilst conducting research into sleep. He attached subjects to an electroencephalogram, which measures brain activity and left them in a darkened room and asked them to relax. When they felt totally relaxed they were to ring a bell. The subjects were given feedback as to whether they had rung the bell at the alpha stage each time and after one day 50% had estimated correctly. On the second day 65% made correct estimations and on the third day 85% and on the fourth day 100%. The researcher repeated the experiment with different subjects and achieved similar results thus demonstrating that brain wave activity could be brought under conscious control.

This is why I asked you to practice the relaxation technique, on a weekly basis, as each session builds on the one before.

Another researcher found that there was a relationship between brainwaves, mood and colours. Subjects were asked to describe how they felt when viewing different coloured lights. It was found that different colours aroused different feelings.

Then the subjects were given feedback as they viewed the coloured lights and they found it was possible to alter their reaction to various colours i.e. the colour red was originally identified with an angry mood but with feedback could be related to calmness.

This identification of colour with mood states is important since we all know how some colour schemes seem to depress us while others uplift us. Nature appears to have got the balance right since green is seen as soothing and calming and also blue.

To return to brainwave activity and the experiment described above in which subjects could change their mood at will, the explanation is that the subjects in the experiment were able to manipulate their brain waves because they had a memory store from the first experiment (colour associated with mood) and a memory store from the second experiment (colour associated with change in mood) and the two memory stores combined into one experience. This experience because it is a memory trace is called an engram and because it is linked to biofeedback activity it is called a BIOGRAM (see page 114)

BIOFEEDBACK, EMOTIONAL AND PSYCHO-SOMATIC PROBLEMS

Earlier in the chapter I described briefly some of the ways in which biofeedback has been used to help with physical problems. Now I would like to just cover its use for emotional and non-organic problems.

Headaches are one of the commonest stress-related complaints and these can range from a mild condition eased by a break from work to the full blown distress of migraine with its accompanying visual disturbance, nausea, pain and disablement.

Biofeedback has been used successfully in the treatment of migraine and tension headaches at the Migraine Clinic in the Birmingham and Midland Eye Hospital with a one year research project financed by the Migraine trust to test the benefits of relaxation to migraine sufferers. 80% had their condition improve.

Galvanic skin resistance biofeedback was used halfway through the project and proved helpful as reinforcement to the existing techniques.

In addition to headaches, biofeedback has been successfully applied to skin problems such as eczema and psoriasis and with respiratory problems such as asthma. It can also be used to help mood modification of irritability, aggression, hostility, fatigue, apathy and depression and for socially embarrassing habits such as bruxism (teeth grinding), stammering, blushing, nervous tics, sweating and insomnia.

Biofeedback is now seen as an alternative to more drastic forms of treatment. Strong and often habit forming drugs, i.e. tranquillisers, pain killers, and barbiturates, whilst alleviating the symptoms, do not remedy the underlying causes of distress and may give rise to undesirable side effects.

Biofeedback has emerged as a proven tool, which can assist both the researchers in the laboratory, the clinical therapist, the engineer and the educationalist. In an ever increasingly complex world it would seem that the remedy of many of the problems facing us can be solved by using the natural resources of the human body, now that we have the knowledge and ability to "tune in" and listen.

DEEP RELAXATION USING IMAGERY (VISUALISATION)

Having explained in simple terms how biofeedback works and the technology that is used, I would like to conclude this section of the chapter with a discussion on imagery and its role in aiding relaxation.

We all know how what we see consciously can affect us and put us in a happy, angry, calm or frustrated mood. For example if we are watching a horse race and we have money on a horse, we will be excited while the race is running, then either disappointed or delighted depending on whether our horse won or lost.

If we are witnesses to a bad car accident, or other disaster we will feel upset, frightened, repelled or shocked. A bank statement with red figures on it has a quite different effect than that with black figures.

If our conscious mind is affected through our vision, then why should not our subconscious mind be affected by our internal vision or imagination?

We know we can visualise all kinds of disasters in our mind and this can make us very worried and sleeplessness at night, by the same method surely we can visualise those images which help to calm us and make us feel more confident!

With practice we can, but most of us find that just at the point when we are emptying our mind of problems another one takes its place unless we have something specific to concentrate on to block out the everyday worries and concerns.

This is why I have prepared the Visualisation Sheets to aid each relaxation session. Naturally by the time you have read the book and practised all ten visualisations - you will be able to draw upon your own imagination and create your own visualisations when you need to relax. Of course if you prefer to continue to use those given in the book please do so, but remember you are only restricted by the breadth of your own imagination.

You can build up a kind of database of your favourite visualisations over time if, as you are going about your business, you allow yourself time to stop and actually "see" some of the pleasanter sights in life. It does not take a lot of effort.

We know that there are unpleasant sights and events going on everyday in the world around us and these issues have to be faced and dealt with, but if we are to cope with the barrage of doom and despondency that daily fills our newspapers and t.v. screens, we need to learn to focus attention on the better and simpler side of life to preserve our internal equilibrium.

MUSIC AS AN AID TO RELAXATION

Music through the years has always been recognised as an important factor in affecting our mood.

When there are important state occasions military and ceremonial music is played to emphasise the solemnity or patriotic atmosphere.

Similarly, when romance is emphasised, the right sort of music is needed to encourage intimacy and a brass band (although very enjoyable on a Sunday afternoon in the park) would not be considered a suitable choice for a quiet dinner for two.

Musicians and therapists have found that there is a correlation between music and relaxation and as a result they have produced some very beautiful recordings which actually encourage the formation of alpha waves in the listener.

You will have heard this type of NEW AGE music as a background to the relaxation audio that comes with this book. I hope that you have found it adds to the process of relaxation as much as previous clients to the course have done. The music on the audio has also been specially recorded to lift the spirits.

Everyone's taste in music varies and the type of music, which you enjoy, might not suit another person. However once you have become used to being truly relaxed you will be able to sense instinctively which types of music reproduce that sensation of relaxation in you.

I recommend that you make a note of sections of music within classical pieces, particularly the slow movements, as these also reproduce the soothing effects required for relaxation.

This is not to denigrate other types of music, all of which have their place as entertainment, to wake us up, as background music etc. but rather to remind you that the aim of relaxation is to lower the arousal system and certain types of music are designed specifically to do the opposite.

Other sounds can also relax such as waves, raindrops, tinkling bells, leaves rustling, birdsong etc. and there are CDs available of these as well as many other natural sounds.

LAUGHTER - AS RELAXATION

It is a well known saying that it takes fewer muscles to smile than to frown! But how many people ever heed this advice?

Laughter and smiling create positive changes in body chemistry, they help to reduce stress and release tension, and this leads on to a general improvement in the body to fight off disease and to improved mental health.

Smiling can be contagious, you only have to look around at an audience in a theatre and once the ice has broken and the show has begun the effects of people on either side smiling and laughing out loud soon begin to enliven even the most miserable soul.

This is why our best known comedians are regarded with such affection by their public. We instinctively know how much better we feel for a good laugh and we appreciate that it is not always easy to make life seem funny without being offensive.

Laughter does not have to arise from professional entertainers alone, it should ideally be a natural part of the human condition. And it is when we are very young. Look how a baby laughs and giggles just with the pure enjoyment of being alive. We were all like that but over the years we have suppressed the natural response to enjoy life.

If you ever have the privilege of being in the company of children or adults with learning disabilities you will be aware of how they are able to laugh and relate to others without any of the inhibitions that we "luckier" people retain.

I know in today's untrusting world saying hello and good morning with a smile to perfect strangers can hold its dangers, but perhaps if we all started with a simple smile and thank you to those with whom we come into contact - whether the person who clips your travel ticket or the newspaper seller, it would create a positive impression. Sometimes it seems that the other person could do with a lesson in smiling too but someone has to make the first move and a smile does take less muscle power than a frown!

SO REMEMBER - LAUGH EVERY DAY

AND KEEP STRESS AT BAY

VISUALISATION NO. 7 - THE ABBEY

Imagine you are walking on the moorland with nothing but the rolling countryside laid out in front of you and the only sounds are of the birds and the grasses being rustled by the wind.

You continue with your exploration of this natural landscape, when floating on the air you hear fragments of human voices. As you walk towards the direction of the sound, the fragments blend into one, a slow melodic chant of male voices in unison.

Suddenly over the next rise you see below you a low grey stone walled building with cultivated land around it. From a distance it could be a small farm but as you glance at the roof you can see a bell tower with a bell glinting in the late afternoon sunlight. From behind the grey stone building darkly cloaked figures emerge, heads bent and hands clasped together. The monks are not aware of your gazing down at them and they continue with their slow and rhythmic chant.

Your eye is drawn to a mound of grey stones on a hillock to the side of the Abbey and it appears to be the ruin of the original site. As you venture down the hillside the monks re-enter the Abbey so you feel free to explore without invading their privacy.

The ruin has just two of its original walls standing with a few foundation stones breaking through the turf to indicate the entrance and there are empty spaces where the windows once were and you can gaze through their emptiness on to the wide vista beyond. The grass has grown up high around the walls and the lichens and mosses have crept into the crevices.

Yet, despite the dereliction, standing here, where peace and harmony have been the focus over the centuries. you feel the sense of continuity, which binds those who lived before, those who are alive today and future generations who will be coming after.

The abbey bell begins to chime and each chime reinforces the sense of continuity and peace, a chime for hope, a chime for reflection, a chime for renewal and a chime for inner life.

VISUALISATION NO. 7 - THE ABBEY

NOW Read the passage again.

PLAY THE AUDIO

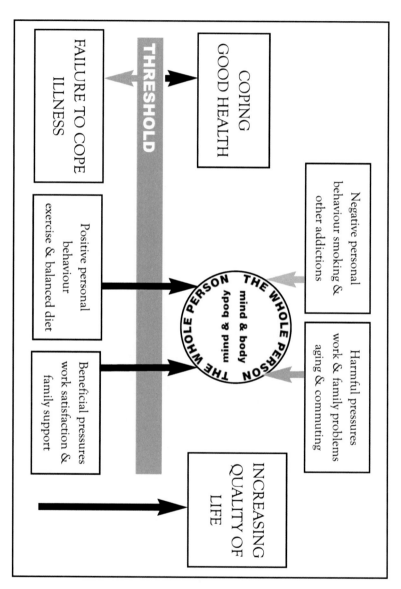

Fig. 13. - FACTORS AFFECTING HEALTH

CHAPTER VIII

FAMILY STRESSES

In this chapter I am going to be discussing the wider areas of stress - not just those which affect us at work but also those which arise from our social and personal life.

If you look at the diagram on *page 124* you will see that each man and woman is a combination of two parts - the physical body and the brain which are composed of nerves and body tissue but which also contains our individual personality. Doctors are now becoming more aware of the interdependence of the two and the practice of holistic medicine, which sees the patient as a whole person rather than a collection of separate organs and tissues is accepted rather more widely now than in the past.

If you look at the diagram on *page 124* you will see that the major factor in a person's ability to stay fit and well is their ability to cope with the stresses of living. The things that cause us stress and drag us down into illhealth are written above the line: -

Negative personal habits such as overeating and
smoking together with pressures brought about by
work and family problems, increasing age and
commuting.

Underneath the line on *page 124* you can see that positive personal habits such as: -

balanced diet and exercise together
with work satisfaction and family/ personal life.

help us to keep fit and healthy and equip us to withstand the pressures day to day living exacts. The large apple on *page 126* represents the 24-hour day and you will see that ideally your day should be properly divided between work/family/social commitments, if you are to retain a balance in your life.

Fig. 14. - ALLOCATION OF TIME

In the context of executive stress it has been shown that in many cases work takes up a disproportionate amount of each 24-hour period and that it spills over into what could be described as social life but it is, in reality, business orientated. Business lunches, dinners, playing golf with business associates, entertaining overseas visitors and clients at home in the evenings or at weekends, all these can be included. Add to these, trips abroad on company business and you would be surprised how much time is spent outside official office hours thinking about work.

PROBLEM AREAS

Below I have listed the problem areas which arise when a partner allows their work to over spill into the hours which should be reserved for leisure and personal relationships.

1. The amount of work the partner brings home in the evenings or at weekends.

2. The absence of the partner in the evening while they are entertaining the company's clients.

3. The assumption that the partner is happy to entertain the company's clients at home.

4. Time spent away travelling on behalf of the company.

5. Frequent moves are part of the job.

On the next page I have listed the reactions of women, both working and full time housewives to their partner's absence. However it must be remembered that whatever the relationships of people who live together in a stable relationship if either person becomes over-involved with work the other will be bound to feel rejected.

Nevertheless those responsible for children will always be more restricted in their ability to socialise and for this reason women's attitudes have been researched regarding partners absence.

Research has shown that on average

1. Working wives - either part time or full time miss their husbands much less than full-time housewives.

2. If the husband travels away frequently on business it is difficult for the wife with children to arrange any social life for herself and she is often lonely in the evenings without someone to share the evening meal.

3. The first two or three weeks are the most difficult when the husband is away but after that the wife and the children adapt.

4. The children's behaviour often changes for the worse and many wives find the disciplinary role is difficult. Schoolwork often suffers. Children across all ages show behaviour changes, except for small babies, but it is the mothers of small babies who miss their husbands more.

5. Adult conversation is missed.

6. Most wives actually enjoy the responsibility of looking after the house and garden and will often do car maintenance and other DIY jobs.

7. The families of men who travel frequently miss them less, they learn to do without them!

8. The greatest stress is felt when the husband travels away shortly after a move to a new house and new social environment.

RELOCATION is one which companies should really bear in mind when promoting and recruiting staff. An analysis of a sample of managers showed that 22% of British managers moved every 2 or 3 years and a further 33% every 5 years, such frequent moves represented a major problem to the whole family. Change of residence was rated as one of the most stressful events.

A CHANGE OF POSITION is also rated as a high cause of stress, because of learning new procedures and fitting in with new colleagues. During this time the executive needs all the support he/she can from their family particularly when, in the worst possible situation, the house is unsold, they are separated from partner and/or family on starting a new job, and have to live in a hotel. Free time is spent eating alone, watching television, searching for a new house and driving long distances at weekends to be with the family for short periods. There is every temptation to buy the first available house but this will not necessarily please the family in the long term.

The wife has major part of the upheaval to bear as she has to set up and furnish a new home, find schools for the children, find babysitters and make new friends. The children will have to adapt too. With all the family under pressure and therefore unable to help each other as much as they should, the company has a responsibility to ease the situation by offering practical help in all aspects of the move.

LIFE CHANGE EVENTS - EFFECTS ON HEALTH

As you will have by now realised, even a change for the better such as promotion can be a source of stress and possible ill health. Researchers Holmes and Rahe studied the effects of change on individuals and asked them to rate various life events in order. They then weighted the individual events and produced a stress scale, which I have reproduced for you on *page 131*. This scale has been tested on different samples of people from Japan, Sweden, Britain and America and it has proved to be valid across these different cultures.

If you wish to check yourself against the scale you should tick any of the events which have occurred to you over the past 6 months or year and add up the individual scores. If you score about 60 for 6 months or 150 for a year, you could understandably be feeling overstressed at the moment. Of course the stress felt will not be exactly the same for each person but this scale does give an useful indication of present levels of stress and can help you plan the future and avoid the build up too many stress making events in too short a period.

HOLMES & RAHE'S STRESS SCALE LIFE CHANGE UNITS

Holmes and Rahe's scale of Life Change Units is a useful tool to measure the amount of stress in your life. By giving arbitrary 50 points to marriage, they calculated a scale of values for events that significantly disturb the pattern of everyday life.

Have any of these events happened to you in the last six months or year? If so, tick each one that has occurred and add up your total score.

Use this scale not just for assessing the past, but planning the future avoiding, as far as possible, a build-up of too many major stress-making events in too short a period.

1. Death of spouse	100	25. Outstanding personal achievement		28
2. Divorce	73	26. Spouse begins or stops work		26
3. Marital separation	65	27. Begin or end school or college		26
4. Prison term	63	28. Change in living conditions		25
5. Death of close family member	63	29. Change in personal habits		24
6. Personal injury or illness	53	30. Trouble with boss		23
7. Marriage	50	31. Change in work hours or conditions		20
8. Fired at work	47	32. Change in residence		20
9. Marital reconciliation.	45	33. Change in school or college		20
10. Retirement	45	34. Change in recreation		19
11. Change in health of family member	44	35. Change in church activities		18
12. Pregnancy	40	36. Change in social activities		18
13. Sex difficulties	39	37. A moderate mortgage or loan		17
14. Gain of new family member	39			
15. Business readjustment.	39			
16. Change in financial state	38			
17. Death of close friend	37			
18. Change to different line of work	36			

19. Change in no. of arguments with spouse	35	38. Change in sleeping habits	16
20. A large mortgage or loan	30	39. Change in the number of family meetings	15
21. Foreclosure of mortgage or loan	30	40. Change in eating habits	15
22. Change in responsibilities at work	29	41. Holiday	13
23. Son or daughter leaving home	29	42. Christmas	12
24. Trouble with in-laws	29	43. Minor violations of the law	11

An example of how the build up of stress can affect the body is shown graphically on below and an explanation given on *page 132*.

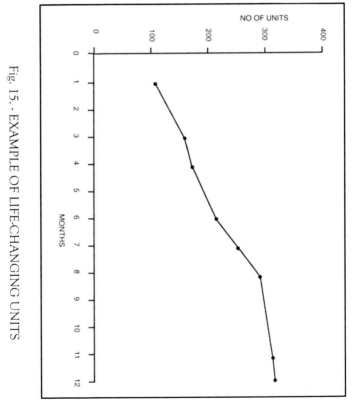

Fig. 15. - EXAMPLE OF LIFE-CHANGING UNITS

318 Life Change Units made up as follows: -

January	(100)	Death of Spouse
March	(53)	Car accident
April	(11)	Licence endorsed
June	(45)	Retirement
July	(38)	Change in financial circumstances
August	(39)	Son marries
November	(20)	Moves to single flat
December	(12)	Christmas (misses wife)
	————	
	(318)	
January		DEPRESSION

The result of these events in a short period of time = mental illhealth i.e.: DEPRESSION

A very sad story which any one of us could face at sometime in later life, so what can be done to help us to cope with the inevitable crises of life?

Where possible we should not try to schedule too much into too short a period of time. Also when unexpected events occur we should give ourselves time to recover from them. This can mean allowing time for us to adapt to a new baby in the house or allowing time to grieve for someone we love who has died.

In the West we are rather reserved when anything requiring an emotional response is needed. If we deny ourselves the opportunity to give free expression to the natural responses of love, joy, anger, grief, empathy and compassion we are denying ourselves the right to LIVE in the true sense.

Western European men are especially prone to take a stiff upper lip approach to any situation, which to a woman would extract an immediate response. This does not mean that men feel any the less but that their conditioning from adolescence has been to repress emotional expression in order to be a proper man.

THE IMPORTANCE OF 'LETTING GO'

While this may indeed prove to be valuable in order to hold on to a man's place in male society and at work, it is from his body's viewpoint extremely damaging, since emotional repression results in tension, which in turn leads to bad health.

Laughing of course is not repressed normally, as this is quite acceptable in males and we all know how good we feel after we have had a good laugh following a comedy film or in the company of people who are having a good time. However the opposite emotional response of crying is taboo in male society which means that men do not have the benefit of the healing properties of tears.

Work by Dr. William Frey found that the chemical in tears is a natural opiate or pain killer. This brain chemical (leucine-enkephalin) pours from the eyes when a person cries. So crying appears to bring about pain relief in physical sense as well as being an emotional outlet.

Of course men do cry even if they will not admit it to anyone else. But whether it is a man or a woman if the need to cry is there it should be allowed to happen, it is not an admittance of failure but rather an acceptance of being HUMAN and alive to feeling. One of the most difficult things in life is to share in someone else's pain and grief but if you can give your time and show your support it will do them far more good than any pills and drugs. This does not mean that these should not be given to the clinically depressed but there is no substitute for human caring.

A PET CAN IMPROVE YOUR HEALTH

Many people have found that in addition to caring offered by others, having an animal to look after can also bring untold benefits and again researchers have shown that PETS can actually improve your health.

HOW A PET CAN IMPROVE YOUR HEALTH

Pets provide us with all sorts of hidden health benefits. I think the first one is that it makes us think about something other than our own worries. We have to remember to feed the pet, care for it when it is ill and give it attention and exercise.

Any dog owner will tell you that it is not only the dog who benefits from the twice daily walk! Owners also have their heart and circulatory system toned up and in all sorts of weather.

Soft animals, such as dogs, cats, rabbits gerbils, hamsters and any pet, which can be stroked, will soothe its owner at the same time. In fact studies have shown that blood pressure can be significantly reduced by owning such a pet through the action of stroking and cuddling.

Other pets have soothing qualities by the nature of the environment in which they live. Owners of tropical fish have realised the calming effects of watching their fish swim around in the aquarium and those who tastes go for outside ponds also enjoy watching goldfish, and other fresh water fish swimming in their pools.

The bird fancier also benefits from his/her pet; they are talked to and in the cases of some species can be trained to "talk" back.

Horses and ponies are another good example where the bond between human and the animal species is made. It is so much easier for people to make a relationship between an animal, which gives so much and asks very little in return except care and love.

Pets are non-judgemental in their response to humans. They love us whether we are rich or poor, in good health or bad and in this respect often prove more loyal than people.

They are also a means of helping those who have difficulty relating to others through age or illness or disability and we can learn a great deal from our pets.

FAMILY RELATIONSHIPS

DIVORCE

As you will see from the Life Event Schedule divorce is the next most stressful event that can occur after the death of a partner.

Although divorce is far more prevalent than in previous decades and the social stigma has largely been reduced it will, because of its many aspects, be the source of stress, particularly at the time immediately preceding and following after the actual divorce date itself.

Even if the divorce is without undue bitterness, the purely practical problems of moving house, coming to acceptable financial arrangements and most importantly, if there are small dependant children, agreeing over custody and visiting rights, add to the emotional load on both the man and the woman involved.

If these practical steps can be undertaken with proper professional advisers and with enough time given to all the parties, both the adults and the children involved, then some of the more traumatic effects of the divorce can be reduced.

All the various changes which may occur quite rapidly within a short time period, i.e. moving home, changing schools for the children, possibly changing work, being in a new neighbourhood away from familiar friends and work colleagues will be stressful to each member of the family.

Everyone reacts differently and two out of three children may settle down with no real problem but the third might have great difficulty with the changes and problem behaviour might occur.

Give everyone time to adjust and do not make too many demands on yourself or on others. If you were suffering a recent bereavement you would be gentle on yourself and a divorce is similar to a bereavement in that a relationship has died even if the people concerned are physically alive and well.

There are various organisations to help families under pressure and it is never an admission of failure to talk to a third party. It is possible that they will be able to give practical help and advice as well as provide an impartial counselling service.

Addresses of agencies who can help with family problems are given at the end on this chapter.

TEENAGERS AND THEIR PROBLEMS

It might seem strange to introduce the problems of teenagers into a book written for men and women at work but as every working parent knows, if you have a problem teenager the problem is not left at home when you leave for work in the morning.

Many parents look forward to the time when their small children will grow up and be less dependant on them and usually by the time children are attending secondary school they are expected to fend reasonably well for themselves.

However just at the point when parents feel they can perhaps sit back and relax, the problems that teenagers can become involved in also become far more serious. This is where the phrase, PARENTAL RESPONSIBILITY, really hits home.

Every parent likes to think that they know how to bring up their own children best but sometimes getting the balance between discipline and freedom is difficult and this is where external advice can be useful.

The guidelines for parents are:

EVERYONE SHOULD KNOW WHAT THE RULES ARE
If necessary write them down ie. so many late nights allowed in a week, time to be in etc.

CONSISTENCY
If the rules are broken, apply sanctions each time, not just when you feel like it.

JUSTICE

Do not differentiate between children-favouritism is the death nell for family harmony.

WHEN IN DOUBT - CHECK

Some teenagers can be very devious in deceiving parents, to them it is part of the thrill.

Often the dangers apparent to an adult are completely disregarded by an otherwise sensible boy or girl.

You will not lose respect by checking - just the opposite - you will show that you are to be taken seriously,

INFORM

This means giving the right information, at the right time, in the right way, about those aspects of life which your child should know about in order to be safe.

This can mean information on sexual matters, drugs, living within society's laws and any aspect of life that your child asks about.

LISTEN

This is the most important part of being a parent.

Most of what teenagers talk about often seems to irrelevant to their parents but it is important to take an interest, because amongst all the trivia one day something needing your attention will be introduced.

TALK WITH YOUR CHILDREN - NOT 'TO' THEM

Try to make time everyday, however limited, to spend time talking together as a family. Do not, if you are a father, delegate this to your wife, as being her job.

Talk also to your children's friends even if you don't entirely approve of them all, how many of your friends did your parents like?

Finally, ACCEPT YOUR RESPONSIBILITY.

We only have our children for a comparatively short time in their whole lives but what we give them as a basis for learning to cope with life is so important. This is one area where we can't pass the buck and blame other people.

Even if your own childhood was not perfect and you inherited problems from your parents, there is no reason why you should not learn from those experiences instead of perpetuating them on through your own family life.

USEFUL ADDRESSES FOR FURTHER INFORMATION ON HELP FOR FAMILIES

The Institute of Family Therapy
24-32 Stephenson Way, London NW1 2HX
www.instituteoffamilytherapy.org.uk
Tel: 0207 391 9150

FOR COUPLES

RELATE
www.relate.org.uk
There are local branches throughout the country

Marriage Care
1 Blythe Mews, Blythe Road, London W14 0NW
www.marriagecare.org.uk
Tel: 0207 371 1341

The Jewish Marriage Council
23 Ravenshurst Road, London NW4 4EE
www.jmc-uk.org
Tel: 0208 203 6311

Scottish Marriage Care
72 Waterloo Street, Glasgow, G2 7DA
www.scottishmarriagecare.org
Tel: 0141 222 2166

PROBLEMS INVOLVING CHILDREN

National Society for the Prevention of Cruelty to Children
Weston House, 42 Curtain Road, London EC2A 3NH
www.nspcc.org.uk
Tel: 0207 825 2500

Gingerbread
307 Borough High Street, London SE1 1JH
Tel: 0207 403 9500
www.gingerbread.org.uk
National support group for single parent families

VISUALISATION NO.8 - THE SEASHORE

*Imagine you are walking along the empty seashore early on a summer's morning. It is
not a commercial holiday resort but just an area of grassy hillocks and sand dunes which
slope down to a sand and shingle shoreline.*

*The beach is deserted except for a man exercising his dog in the distance.
The large black dog obviously has no aversion to water as he runs
in repeatedly to fetch a stick thrown by his master into the ebbing tide.*

*On the breakwater's wooden arms which are becoming gradually more and more prominent
as the water recedes,
you watch the seagulls and cormorants balancing in the early morning sunshine. They, of
course, are looking for their breakfast and the sandpipers are waiting patiently until it is
time for them to investigate the tasty morsels lying just beneath the surface of the tide
washed sand.*

*The only noise you can hear is the crying of the seabirds,
the occasional bark of the black dog and the
swoosh, swoosh of the waves breaking gently on the beach.*

*The sun is getting higher in the sky now and the warmth is beginning to penetrate
through your clothing and on to your face.
You raise your face to the sun and at the same time you breath deeply.
You can smell the seaweed and the tang of the sea and feel
the salt from the seaspray drying on your skin.*

*The rhythmic swoosh, swoosh of the waves is beginning to form a continuous pattern in
your brain and you take time to sit down facing the horizon and allow
the effects of the fresh air, the clean smell of the sea and
the sound of the waves permeate through all your body.
You watch the different wave patterns as they break on the shore.
The larger waves with white tipped crests and the gentle under waves, which merely lap
gently like lemonade froth on the glistening sand beneath.*

*As you sit there you can feel the tension in your body melting away and
your mind becoming clear and refreshed as the beach itself after
its nightly cleansing by the high tide.*

VISUALISATION NO.8 - THE SEASHORE

NOW Read the passage again.

PLAY THE AUDIO

CHAPTER IX

In this chapter I will be explaining how we face certain fundamental changes in our working life which can cause stress, namely the midlife crisis, redundancy and retirement.

MIDLIFE CRISIS

Firstly the midlife crisis. You may have heard people talk about this - probably jokingly about a colleague who suddenly seems to be acting out of character - or maybe you have thought it was just a myth dreamed up to explain why middle-aged men suddenly start chasing young secretaries round the office. However it is a fact that once a person (male or female) reaches the age of 50 they find that the way they approached life up to then has undergone subtle changes and, without them realising the fact, they have become middle-aged. It happens to us all, we all recognise the feeling when the doctors in hospitals are our age or younger, policemen are youths with helmets held up by their ears and our own children start to refer to anything that happened more than 10 years ago as back in history.

The middle years of life can be a specially difficult time for women as they have to bear the changes in their hormonal system and, even if they are lucky to pass through the menopause with few troublesome physical symptoms, they have the psychological pressures of knowing that their reproductive life is ceasing, which in men is a later and more slower occurrence.

Where both partners are of similar age and are experiencing the sensation of being at the 'mid point' in life tension often occurs as the partner is a mirror image of the process of ageing which is happening to oneself. Hence the attraction of other more youthful companions which provide an image of life and vitality.

This is a very common and understandable human reaction but whether a couple wishes to revitalise their relationship or an individual wants to perk up his/her own morale, the physical aspects of growing older can of course be minimised.

We can take a fresh look at our bodies and we can slim down, tone up muscles, acquire a tan, try a new hairstyle etc. This was in the past the typical female response but equality has meant that men too are now expected to keep up appearances which has its benefits in terms of self-image in the work place as well as producing a positive response from the ladies.

On *pages 157-159* I have covered the most important aspects of men's health, as these do not receive as much coverage as women's health. If you are male please read this, as it is important.

More difficult than changing physical appearance, is changing attitude, particularly as you get older. Yet someone who is at it were 'stuck' in beliefs and prejudices which were acquired some 20 or more years ago, will find it difficult to communicate with the generation following on. Keeping an open mind and being ready to listen to another point of view especially when given by a younger person is the sign of someone whose response has not been frozen into a set pattern. This is where, if you do have teenage children or come into contact with young adults, you should try to spend some time listening to what they have to say, and even if some of it is outrageous, at the same age were you spouting pearls of wisdom?

One of the areas in which our attitudes may have changed over time is that of our enthusiasm and commitment to our work. Some people are fortunate in that their chosen profession or career remains as fulfiling and stimulating after 20 years as in the beginning. For the majority the initial enthusiasm will fade away with the years but the security of knowing the job well and the friendship of colleagues built up over time, compensates for the lack of sparkle.

There are however a minority who realise in middleage that their work is so unfulfilling now compared to 20 years ago that they would much rather move to another occupation which really interests them. This is sometimes their original choice of occupation, which, because of family pressure and circumstances, they were unable to follow through or it is simply that their aspirations have changed or that they have become disillusioned with their present occupation.

These people are in a very stressful position because they are faced with the choice of giving up a financially rewarding and secure career and all that this means to their family, particularly the wife if she managed the family through the lean years and is now looking forward to a time without financial pressures, for what might be termed by others a pipedream.

Against this they have to balance the prospect of working at a job they no longer enjoy and may actually detest. This is where professional counselling can be well worth seeking as a wrong decision could cause much pain in the future

Unfortunately, sometimes change is something which we cannot choose for ourselves but is thrust upon us and, in regard to our work this is usually in the form of redundancy. At one time, to be without a job, particularly if you were a white-collar worker, invited stigmatisation and men would not let friends or neighbours know for fear of loss of status

.

REDUNDANCY

Nowadays, however with a very volatile job market where mergers and company buyouts are common place affecting business executives as much as unskilled workers, this attitude is being modified. Nevertheless, even if one receives sympathy rather than scorn, it is still a very unsettling experience to be made redundant. Even when you know that it was not a reflection of your work performance (for example when two companies merge and the excess staff are unloaded) there is still a feeling of vulnerability mixed with disbelief, anger and bitterness. Of course the longer a person has been with a company the more settled they have become and therefore it can often affect them more strongly.

The best advice if this should happen is DON'T PANIC. Remember that this has happened to other people, many of whom have used the experience to rethink their lives and their priorities, and who have emerged in some cases with new careers and increased quality of life, even if there has been a reduction in salary.

THE JOB CENTRE

There will be of course the feeling of numbness, broken by spells of relief and even euphoria at getting the blow over, especially where there have been signs of change for some months anger and resentment will also follow but after this there is a period of adjustment. On *page 150* I have given a list of ways to cope with the initial shock of redundancy.

It has been shown that an executive between the ages of 35 and 45 will take up to 9 months to find new employment and for those over 45 it can take up to 2 years - so they will have to come to terms with a lengthy period of job hunting. Unfortunately for those who are near 50 because of the undoubted policy of discrimination against older workers (ageism) being employed again in the same type of position as that before redundancy is virtually impossible. In fact many companies now operate an unofficial retirement age of 50 years despite the fact that those who joined in their youth expected to retire at the normal official retirement age and to which end they had paid in their pension contributions.

This practice of ageism may hopefully in the future be legislated against in the same way that discrimination due to sex or race is against the law, but until that happens society will be left with a mass of well trained, very experienced men and women whose only crime is that they have grown old in employers' eyes because of the accent on youth and dynamism. Some companies have introduced schemes to take on older workers but this usually means working at unskilled jobs which are not suited to those who have been used to management positions.

The most usual route for the older redundant executive is into self-employment as a consultant or to join together with a group of colleagues who have also been released together from a large company to form their own company. This can be a very fulfiling and financially viable solution providing it is thought through carefully in the initial stages.

NEVER TOO OLD OR YOUNG TO LEARN

RETRAINING

This can seem at first to be irrelevant to those over 45, for whom the number of years left until retirement age is limited. However many people have proved that it is never too late to learn new skills, whether academic or vocational, and life experience and maturity compensate for any lack of speed. In fact often the older worker will prove to be more accurate and conscientious. The main problem is finding out what training facilities are available and the financial arrangements, whether government assisted or privately funded and having a positive attitude to acquiring new skills.

RE-EDUCATION

This is also a form of retraining in that those who either left school without the necessary qualifications or who would have preferred to study other subjects but who did not have the opportunity, can go back and study either for pleasure or in order to move into a different area of work. This is now possible since many polytechnics, colleges and universities will accept students, even those without the usual basic educational requirements, as they appreciate that mature students can contribute as much to student life as those who are twenty years younger. Many older students attain creditable passes in examination subjects, which they were unable to take when they themselves were young.

VOLUNTARY SERVICE OVERSEAS

The British Executive Service Overseas provides a volunteer executive service to developing countries - no pay but travelling living and other expenses are found for the executive and spouse.

This is an option for those who either have work experience in a particular part of the world and can use that to help that country's economy or who simply wish to share their skills and broaden their horizons now that they have the opportunity to do so.

USEFUL GUIDELINES FOR COPING WITH REDUNDANCY

1. DON'T PANIC

2. If married, talk to your partner first. They may be stunned but they would rather hear the news direct from you than through a third party.

3. Discuss it with your family and friends. You need their support now and this will show you who your true friends are.

4. Keep fit - eat less but wholesome food. Take plenty of exercise and keep in good physical shape.

5. Keep mentally alert, carry on with hobbies, reading courses and conferences, visit exhibitions, take on short term teaching assignments and possibly write technical articles for journals.

6. Get good professional advice on redundancy payments, golden handshakes or payments in lieu of notice.

7. Sit down and list your main qualifications and personal qualities and how they relate to the type of position sought. If uncertain, ask a friend or colleague to assess you (provided they can be objective).

8. Take promises of employment by business acquaintances in the early days of redundancy with a pinch of salt, unless of course you are so well known and prestigious that other firms have been headhunting you prior to the redundancy.

9. Make a plan of action. This should cover: -

   a) immediate finances
   b) longer term finances - i.e. up to 2 years
   c) independent assessment of personal and business qualifications
   d) production of an up-to-date c.v.
   e) where to look for work, minimum salary required to cover basic outgoings
   f) consider other forms of work. i.e. freelancing, partnership, consultancy, etc.

10. Join an existing support group for unemployed executives or, if there isn't one in your area, why not start one?

RETIREMENT

Having looked that the negative side of change at work redundancy - let us now think about the more positive side - normal retirement. If a man or woman has been fortunate enough to keep working until official retirement age of 60 or 65, they should be looking forward to a chance to take life much easier. Some executives are of course retired earlier than this, either because of health problems or because they wish to have the chance of second careers.

It has been said that you should plan your retirement three years ahead or, at the very minimum, twelve months. However many people put off thinking seriously about what retirement will mean in practical terms for them until it is almost upon them. Why this reluctance? It lies in the degree to which people identify with their work and how much their work provides them with status and self-fulfilment. The unskilled labourer is only too pleased to end his hard physical working life in order to spend more time on his hobbies and with his friends. In contrast the high pressure business executive instinctively knows that he/she will miss the constant change, the challenges and fresh projects of the business world and therefore puts retirement to the back of his mind assuming that he/she will be able to handle it when it comes.

However, when the day finally does come and he or she has had the final leaving party, the presentations and the speeches are over, they begin to realise that life is no longer ever going to be quite the same again. And if it is going to be different for the executive it is also going to be different for their partner.

This is because of the separate life styles that work imposes on people who live together. For both husband and wife the early years before marriage would have been mainly centred round their parents and family, school and college friends. Then they meet and and they have a combined social life. After marriage the wife may also continue in her work and enjoy a social life associated with it and her husband will have social activity concerned with his business affairs or sporting interests. She may of course in time stay at home bringing up the family and exchange a formal social life associated with work to a more informal one as a result of voluntary or part-time work, PTA's church and women's clubs etc.

These phases in a woman's life are flexible in that she may start a family late in life, she may give up work and then return to it later, or she may manage to combine work and bringing up a family. The appearance of children, can cause the social life of the man and woman to divide, since it is usually rather difficult for couples with small children to attend social functions together.

For men life follows a more rigid pattern with college, university, business school or the armed forces, followed by work which, particularly if a TYPE A personality is involved, will provide also the main part of his social activities. This period of a man's life, if he is fortunate not have suffered redundancy will continue uninterrupted for over 40 years until retirement age. Which brings us back to the executive who has now said goodbye to all his colleagues and who is leaving the office for home for the last time.

Like many people who have worked hard for their living over the years, he and his wife will have probably planned a nice holiday, something special, perhaps a cruise, which will take up the first few weeks or months of the retirement. But what happens once they are back at home together all day, assuming of course that the wife is no longer working, when he is there every minute demanding endless cups of tea and coffee and wanting to know when lunch will be ready? So many men fail to realise that while they have been away at the office busy building empires, their wives have also been building up their own social and working lives. For domestic harmony the man who retires must take into account his wife's right to a social life and not expect her to direct her life solely round him now that he is home all day.

This is where pre-retirement planning is important because there are so many activities, which the retired person can enjoy, but they need some forethought. On *page 155* I have listed some useful addresses for those who are pre-retirement. These are for organisations who can offer practical help for the retired as well as job opportunities - part time or voluntary - and also useful leaflets and books which provide good background reading. On *page 156* I have also listed 10 points to a happy retirement.

Retirement is mainly one of attitude. If you tell yourself you are going to enjoy it, then it is very likely that you will. However if you spend your days talking endlessly about your past achievements at work you will bore your new acquaintances and lose the chance of friendship. So far better to have a real interest in what is happening around you in the present to get real enjoyment out of life.

Good health is obviously an important factor and this is the time when good health patterns formed in middle age will pay dividends. Commonsense should also prevail so that however much you and your wife love the family home, if it is too big for just the two of you, you should consider moving into somewhere smaller and easier to maintain, and preferably all on one level, since most accidents to women over 65 are caused by stairs.

Ideally as you adapt as a couple to retirement, you will find a new routine to life, one which combines outside interests for you both while also allowing you the time to discover the interests you can both share together. Of course one of the best-combined interest is that of grandchildren, which is one of the bonuses of later life.

Do make the effort to take up some form of physical exercise, as this is essential to keep the body from becoming prematurely old. Brisk walking with the dog, playing bowls swimming (there are special sessions for older people at most swimming pools) dancing, even if you have not been a dancer previously, will all help to keep the muscles toned up and also create a social life.

Many people feel too as they reach this stage of life that they would like to be able to put something back into the community and to help others less fortunate with their life experience. Many charities and voluntary organisations would not be able to operate if it were not for their unpaid work force and there are a wide variety of tasks, from driving people to and from hospital appointments, fund raising, committee work. youth work etc. The local library usually will have a register of voluntary organisations and these are welcoming of new members.

ENJOYING YOUR GRANDCHILDREN

USEFUL ADDRESSES FOR FURTHER INFORMATION

1. British Executive Service Overseas (BESO)
164 Vauxhall Bridge Road
London SW1V 2RB
www.beso.org
Tel: 0207 630 0644
Provides a volunteer executive service to developing countries - no pay but travelling, living and other expenses are found for executive and spouse.

2. Life Academy
9 Chesham Road, Guildford
Surrey GU1 3LS
www.life-academy.co.uk
Tel: 01483 301170
30 associated local Retirement and Pre-retirement Associations linked together as the Pre-retirement Association of Great Britain and Northern Ireland. Courses, booklet and free advice.

3. Voluntary Worker Organiser Local Council of Social Services.
Voluntary workers are always needed in a wide variety of jobs, from driving handicapped children to school, Meals on Wheels, practical help to the housebound etc.

4. The Retired and Senior Volunteer Programme
Head Office: 237 Pentonville Road
London N19NJ
www.csv-rsvp.org.uk
Tel: 0207 643 1385   (to find your local branch)
National organisation which recognises that older people have a lifetime of skills to offer

Books to read:-
1. "What every woman should know about retirement" Ed. Helen Franks
   Pub. Age Concern England 1987
2. "Handbook for Retirement" John Kemp and Bill Tadd
   Pub. Macmillan 1987 (Good for financial planning)
3. "Unretirement" Catherine Dorton Fyock and Ann Dorton
   Pub. AMACOM (USA) 1994
4. "Jobs for the over 50's Linda Greenbury Pub. Platkus 1994

TEN POINTS TO A HAPPY RETIREMENT

1. Do not cease to be active just because you have retired.

2. Do a job of some kind, preferably one that helps others.

3. Do not be tempted by endless leisure otherwise boredom and lassitude set in.

4. Prepare for retirement at least a year in advance (where possible).

5. Accept retirement and do not try to hang on in fulltime work which can be a degrading experience.

6. Eat and drink in moderation to enjoy and long and healthy retirement.

7. Don't mix only with one's contemporaries but enjoy the company of young people whenever possible in order to keep a youthful outlook.

8. Never begin a conversation with "when I was your age".

9. Do not go to extremes - practise a relaxed attitude and lively interest in others.

10. Keep a check on financial matters in order to avoid stringency in later years.

ABOVE ALL - REMEMBER TO ENJOY LIFE

MALE HEALTH PROBLEMS

Men and women share the same problems in regard to their health, as apart from the reproductive system, they are the same. The main difference is that women are programmed from an early age to seek the advice of their doctor or health visitor or clinic whereas men tend to only go to the doctor as a last resort, usually driven by fear or desperation or by the woman in his life persuading him to do so.

This reluctance to seek medical advice and also to be excluded from the barrage of health advice and education aimed at women through television and magazines means that many men are rather misinformed about their bodies and health issues. There is also the tradition that illness represents vulnerability and this does not equate with "maleness" in our society.

If men are reluctant to seek advice on non-intimate medical problems then it is no surprise that they will avoid at all costs talking about anything connected with a lack of sexual drive or performance or those parts of the male body connected with urination or erection.

Like every other part of the human body, there is the natural tendency to take for granted a function until it stops functioning as normal and this is no different when it comes to sexual organs. The problem should be looked at as any other medical problem. In fact it is best seen in this context since sexual problems in the male usually arise from some medical reason which can be treated. i.e. diabetes, high blood pressure, side effects of medication, alcoholism, arteriosclerosis, and neurological disease. Less than 10% are due to psychological causes such as stress.

Age will cause some decrease in frequency but not necessarily in performance and therefore it is important that any man who is having problems in sexual function or with the urinary tract seeks medical advice, and does not put it down to "getting older". Even a simple urinary infection will need some treatment and the doctor will be able to decide whether or not a course of antibiotics is all that is needed or referral to a specialist.

The regular medical checks that some companies now insist on are ideal opportunities for a man to voice any fears or doubts he may have on any part of his health. It is far better to express these than bottle them up where worry itself can produce its own symptoms. If in doubt ASK is the best advice.

MALE MENOPAUSE - FACT OR FICTION?

The idea of a male menopause is usually ridiculed by most men, including many doctors, because the male does not have a distinct cessation in hormonal activity such as the ending of periods in women. However there is growing acceptance of a group of symptoms, which cluster together around the age of 50 (give or take 5 years either way).

These symptoms appear to affect most men and, although sexual dysfunction can be one of the most obvious to the man involved and his partner, the other symptoms are equally troublesome.

These include:

Weight gain (an increase in weight and change in eating pattern in a man who has held a steady weight for many years)

Lethargy, apathy and general lack of interest in life

Depression (mild right through to severe even suicidal depression)

Irritability and intolerance

Reduced creativity

Increased frequency of urination

Lack of sexual interest

Becoming inward looking, evaluating contribution to life, facing own mortality.

These symptoms are described by Dr. Malcolm Carruthers as a Viropause, and are caused by a combination of factors, one of which can be a drop in testosterone (the male sex hormone), the others being alcohol consumption, stress, prostrate trouble, and/or other physical problems. Dr. Carruthers advocates a screening programme for men in whom the symptoms are pronounced and which are causing domestic and work problems. He also believes that the male equivalent of HRT can be given to men who show clinical signs of needing it, providing proper checks are made. He operates a private clinic in Harley Street where male healthchecks and appropriate treatment can be arranged.

However such attitudes are not prevalent amongst other doctors and NHS doctors will only treat the physical symptoms i.e. impotence with physical methods.

This is done by injection to cause an erection but which may need an antidote given by the local hospital if the erection does not go down within a certain time period. This can obviously be a drawback to spontaneous intercourse as well as embarrassing for the man concerned.

VIAGRA:

Since this book was begun a new drug for erectile dysfunction has come on to the market and received a lot of publicity. The drug is a breakthrough in that it is taken orally and eliminates the necessity for the injections described above. Because of the numbers of men suffering from impotence in the UK it can only be prescribed under the NHS by a doctor, if he feels that certain clinical conditions can be met. However it is available privately and many men have taken advantage of the new medication. The drug is not without side effects and taken in conjunction with other medication Viagra can be fatal so it is essential that a proper medical screening takes place before the drug is prescribed.

It is important therefore that men who feel that they are not being treated adequately should ask for second opinions and educate themselves about their own health. If they feel that certain forms of treatment are being denied them, then they will have to do what women have done over the years, ask until they are provided.

The lowering of taboos about discussing male health and in particular male sexual problems would help enormously in dispelling ignorance and fear and would enable both partners in a sexual relationship to discuss the problems instead of ignoring them which builds a wall between them.

Women are, from adolescence onwards, aware of the fluctuation in sexual desire through the monthly cycle and also in pregnancy and again in the menopause but a man's sexual needs are seen to be constant over time and, when young, ad infinitum! It can come therefore as a shock to both partners when male sexual needs change without any obvious cause.

Learning to adapt to change has been covered earlier in this chapter and sexual needs are one area where adaptation has to start for both sexes if harmony is to reign. It is rather like going into adolescence again and having to re-learn what makes you and your partner happy.

Like adolescence it can be quite turmoil but eventually new patterns of loving will emerge and if the relationship is strong it will survive. After all the one element in life we all share regardless of everything else is growing older, so we can surely empathise with each other over this.

VISUALISATION NO. 9 - MEMORIES

Allow your mind to empty itself of the day to day preoccupations and allow those half-forgotten and hazy recollections of your past to drift in and out.

Those memories of childhood, adolescence and young adulthood which have been buried deep below the necessity of everyday living - let them gradually emerge into your consciousness.

Perhaps some of those memories are pleasant, bringing a smile to your lips and perhaps some are unpleasant, which is why they have been pushed down out of your conscious mind. But all these memories are the recording of your life and the events and people who have made you what you are today.

We start life with our dreams and aspirations and, depending on our circumstances, we gradually compromise and alter these dreams to fit what is practical to achieve. As we grow older our dreams change as we do and the value we place on each dream changes too.

Think about your dreams and whether they are still the same, have you achieved them or did you exchange them for different dreams as your life experience grew? Can you see your life as a nicely patterned carpet with all the threads carefully inter-woven or are there threadbare patches, which need attention?

Now in your mind let your hand reach out and pull a loose thread at the edge of the carpet and as the thread begins to unravel, let your imagination drift along the ever-lengthening thread until you reach that part of the carpet where you feel your are most content. Let yourself dwell in that contentment and, as you feel warm and contented, you know that you have found that aspect of your life, which for you holds the most value.

VISUALISATION NO. 9 - MEMORIES

NOW Read the passage again.

PLAY THE AUDIO

CHAPTER X

STRESS & THE WOMAN AT WORK

During the previous nine chapters I have been at pains to include women as well as men in my writing but at times it has been necessary to refer to the male sex specifically because the data and statistics have been based on men only. However now I hope to redress the balance a little by devoting a whole chapter to women at work and how stress can affect them.

Although the data given below refers to women business executives, the findings can be applied to women in any profession, i.e. Law, Medicine, Science, Technology, etc. where there are hierarchies, set routes to promotion and a work culture originally male only.

There was a very interesting study published in 1984 by Davidson and Cooper of the University of Manchester Institute of Science and Technology, which set down the findings of research into occupational stress in female managers compared with male managers.

A sample of 696 female managers and 185 male managers were asked to complete questionnaires and in depth interviews were given to 60 female managers from supervisory, junior, middle and senior grades. The results showed that women in junior and middle management experienced the highest overall stress followed by male supervisors, senior women managers, male junior managers, female supervisors and male middle managers and finally senior male managers, who reported the lowest stress levels. So it would appear that women experience more stress the higher they go in business, whereas men experience less in comparison as they rise through the ranks. Why should this be?

The Business of Learning to Relax

The role of women in society is radically changing in most Western countries. The economic pressures of inflation, the influence of the women's movement and the need to develop self-identity are encouraging women to take a more active role outside the home, to pursue full-time careers or education or to participate more widely in society generally. Certainly a large number of women who work full time are also aspiring to climb the same organisational ladders as their male counterparts.

With more women now working than ever before, there is also an enormous growth in younger women entering many of the formerly male dominated jobs, including the field of management. In the U.S., with the strongest legislation affecting the employment of women, 23.6% of managers and administrators are women, followed by the U.K. with 18.8%. Even so, in the U.K., the occupations in which women are most likely to be managers are traditionally female occupations such as retailing, catering and personnel.

It is of interest to note that a British survey of 770 female management students found that 43% believed that there was a distinct disadvantage in being a woman and desiring careers in management. Although it seemed easy enough for women to gain employment at the lower rungs of the organisational ladders, it proves very difficult for them to reach middle and senior positions.

Thus those women who enter managerial positions are a minority group subjected to male dominated policy making and female managers are subjected to a greater number of work related pressures compared to men. This is particular significance when you consider that, firstly the job of management has been isolated as being a high stress occupation for males, and secondly that female managers have listed being able to cope with pressure as an important factor contributing to their success.

On the next page I have set out the profile of the average women manager - how do you measure up to this profile?

Is this a profile, which you would wish to identify with in future years?

What aspect of the profile would you wish to alter in your particular case.?

If you cannot identify yourself with the profile, are there any women in your working environment who you think do fit the description broadly given?

Can you compare, in your working environment, a woman manager and a male manager doing broadly similar work?

PROFILE OF THE AVERAGE FEMALE MANAGER

She could be married (43%), single (43%) or divorced or widowed (15%).

She is less likely to have children than a male manager and more likely to have step-children.

She is responsible for 600 people or more.

She receives a salary sometimes commensurate with that of a male manager doing the same job but often only 2/3 of the salary paid to a man doing similar work.

She is more likely to be in full-time employment than other female workers.

Her average length of employment is 20.8 years of which 9 years is spent with the same company.

She is well educated with a university degree (46%) a Masters Degree (22%) or Doctorate (3.7%).

Summary :
She is 40 years old, highly educated, employed full-time and has tended not to discontinue her working career pattern (even if she has married and has a family).

Why should women be aware of the stress that they are under, surely it is only men who have heart attacks in their middle years due to stress?

This is a common fallacy and many women do not realise that heart disease is just as common as all forms of cancer together in women, as many women die from coronary heart disease as from breast and cervical cancer.

Men do have a higher risk, three times that of premenopausal women, but it is still the number one cause of death in women in Britain. When a woman reaches the menopause the oestrogen hormone declines and this then raises the risk to nearly the same as for the male population. HRT can protect the heart and arteries and advice on this should be sought from your GP or through a WELL Woman clinic.

Blood pressure and cholesterol levels should be measured over the age of 35 and particularly in the years leading up to and into the menopause. Obviously any hereditary risk of heart disease should be brought to the attention of the doctor.

IF YOU EXPERIENCE CHEST PAINS ALWAYS INSIST ON A MEDICAL CHECK-UP

Do not be afraid to ask for an electrocardiogram, as many doctors do not recognise heart disease in their women patients because of the assumption that it is a male problem.

THE IMPORTANCE OF DIET AND EXERCISE

Diet and exercise are the two areas, as well as giving up smoking, where women can take control possibly better than men, if only because they are used to thinking about their body shape and are usually responsible for the family meals.

A mediterranean type diet of fresh fruit, vegetables, fish and oil inside of fat for cooking is to be recommended, together with sensible regular exercise.

AWARENESS OF STRESS ARISING FROM WORK

As women are as vulnerable to men to illness caused by stress, it is important to now look at the sources of this stress, particularly as it arises in the work place.

On the following page I have produced a list of the sources of stress on female managers and the symptoms that these produce.

SOURCES OF STRESS ON FEMALE MANAGERS

1. Executive role expectations

2. Patron male boss

3. Threatened male colleagues

4. Blocked promotion

5. Threat of sexual involvement

6. 'Queen Bee' boss

7. 'Wonder Woman' syndrome managing home and work

SYMPTOMS OF STRAIN

1. Tiredness

2. Anxiety attacks

3. Migraine headaches

4. Excessive drinking and/or smoking

5. Irritation

6. Tension (neck or back)

7. Sleeplessness

8. Frustration or dissatisfaction

Let us examine the sources of stress in more detail, starting with ROLE EXPECTATIONS.

These include the sex-stereotyped behaviours and attitudes that most women carry around with them from their early upbringing. Some of the more prominent ones in this area are conflict about working and raising a family, about 'being the boss', about 'being ambitious and aggressive in business dealings' etc. This culture trap creates difficulties for women at work since more organisations are still dominated by male values and behaviours and women are still encouraged to play out a less achievement orientated role than men.

One of the women interviewed by Davidson and Cooper remarked "I find it very difficult being the boss and when I go out with the staff socially and am introduced as 'the boss' that embarrasses me. I don't want to be introduced as anybody's boss. Another interesting comment came from a senior female manager who said 'I think a lot of women have a built-in failure factor. They feel that they shouldn't compete because they are women and so they don't."

In the work environment there is a fundamental difficulty in trying to meet the role expectations of being an executive. Since the executive role has been in the past perceived by both men and most women a fundamentally a male role, any individual female manager is unlikely to be seen as adequately fitting or meeting the role requirements.

Those women who do adopt a 'masculine approach' often sacrifice those qualities of warmth, compassion and empathy, which normally bring a balance into the work place. Trying to tread a fine line between retaining respect for their intellectual skills and authority without losing touch with their feminine side is extremely difficult, particularly where any softness is seized upon as a sign of weakness by their male colleagues.

PATRON MALE BOSS

Frequently a male boss adopts a patron role vis-à-vis his immediate subordinate, protecting and advising her but at the same time using her competence for his own advancement. This can cause enormous stress on the female manager concerned because she feels she much constantly perform at her best to meet his expectations. She becomes identified with him and suffers the whims and circumstances that befall him, her own individual talents and abilities are not always recognised by others, but get fused with the boss's strengths and weaknesses and she is still playing out her dependent role and not trying to make her mark on the basis of her own resources.

THREATENED MALE COLLEAGUES

There is the potential threat that many male managers feel about the competence of their female colleagues. Indeed in an effort to overcome feelings of insecurity, inadequacy and to meet a variety of internal role expectations, many female managers work harder, longer and more thoroughly than their male counterparts or even their male bosses.

BLOCKED PROMOTION

This is one of the most serious problems women in management face. For the vast majority of women who are struggling for individual recognition and achievement, the road up the executive ladder is not so easy. they face blockages at all levels as well as difficulties in combining their home and office life.

Currently many promotional advances in industry are based on the availability of managers to be mobile to move from one site to another, from one country to another. This is a major stumbling block for any married female manager and one that most organisations have failed to address. In addition to job transfers, managers are also expected to be available for short term assignment abroad or in other parts of the country. Once again, female managers with families are unable to offer their services and this counts against them when promotion is being considered

It is customary to talk of the "glass ceiling" beyond which the women executive cannot pass. This is not a tangible blockage written down in company policy but a underlying resistance by the male sex to allow any woman, however brilliant, to rise to the highest levels of power within an organisation. Where the glass ceiling is broken through it is usually through the woman owning or starting the company herself, or having attributes which enable her to overcome all male resistance.

SEXUAL HARASSMENT

Now to a very sensitive issue. Sexual politics in the office. Female managers also have the additional burden of being used or using their sexuality in office politics or career development. The pressure of sexual harassment, such as advances or exploitation can create serious problems in the work environment.

The City of London appears to have the most overt sexual harassment centred around the financial institutions and the dealing rooms especially. Scandals brought to public attention through the media in the early nineties have exposed the locker room mentality which is rife in City institutions. Those women who do survive may risk becoming hardened in order to compete with the men they work alongside. Interestingly when comparisons are drawn with EEC counterparts it is only the Englishmen who have such a crass attitude to women.

HOW TO DEAL WITH HARASSMENT AND DISCRIMINATION:-
Complaints about sexual harassment to the Equal Opportunities Commission have risen steadily from 427 in 1991 to 793 in 1993. In 1991, 32 cases were heard and 41 percent were successful; in 1993 58 cases were heard and 45 percent were successful.

Keep a record. Put a complaints about harassment on record; write a letter to the perpetrator; stating your objections, and keep a copy; make a diary of what happens; tell somebody close, inside or outside the workplace, what is going on. This way you will have evidence if you choose to go to tribunal.

You can get advice from the Equal Opportunities Commission (tel: 0845 601 5901) and Law Centres (the number of your local Law Centre is in the telephone directory). If you decide to take your employer to industrial tribunal you must make application within three months of the last incident of discrimination.

For racial abuse there is The Commission for Racial Equality the telephone number of which is 0207 939 0000.

THE QUEEN BEE BOSS

This occurs when a junior women executive tries to cope with an aggressive workaholic boss. Many successful women who have achieved positions of influence in organisations have done so by inhibiting many of their female traits and attitudes. In many cases however, underneath the facade of the dominant woman boss is still a very insecure and less than confident women.

This combination of surface behaviour and hidden feelings sometimes produces a rather frightening and intimidating figure to junior female managers. The Queen Bee worked hard to attain her status and frequently feels why should it be easier for them and pushes her female subordinates more than her male ones.

THE WONDERWOMAN SYNDROME

Finally the most potentially intractable source of stress in women in management is trying to manage home and work simultaneously. Although many husbands and partners intellectually accept and encourage their wives in their careers, few give continuous practical support. Many men come from homes where their role model of the ideal women was a mother who either was a full-time housewife or who worked combining a job with housework. Therefore the fact that they still expect their working wives to carry out the traditional domestic duties is not surprising.

Now we have looked at the sources of stress for women at work what can I advise to help women tackle the stresses they are under? Firstly I will set out below how I feel that organisations can help women and secondly I will advise how women themselves can take control over their response to stressful situations.

WHAT CAN ORGANIZATIONS DO TO HELP THE FEMALE MANAGER OF THE FUTURE?

POLICY CHANGES

Allowing a more flexible working week for women, so that they can arrange their work and home commitments accordingly. This might mean more part time posts or job share of merely a flexible-working schedule. (With the advent of information technology and the ability of home working on computers increasing this is quite a feasible option)

Paternity and maternity leaves. With the increase in dual-career managerial families, there will have to be more considerate and flexible policies that enable women to have children or cope with family crises, within natural limits, without loss of employment entitlements.

Day nursery facilities. Increasingly throughout Europe organisations are beginning to provide in-house day care centres for the children of their employees. Since governments have not taken on this responsibility employers will have to, at least in the short term.

Change in relocation policies. This will have to happen from two points of view. First to allow women managers the opportunity of promotion without moving. Secondly to accommodate the needs of dual-career managerial families, when one is offered a move and the other is not. Men and women should have the 'right to refuse' without their career being put in jeopardy. This would allow normal home life to be maintained without the career of one partner or the other being 'sacrificed' for the sake of the other.

PROVIDING CAREER OPPORTUNITIES FOR FEMALE MANAGERS

i.   Career planning and counselling. Because of the special needs and circumstances of some women, it is necessary to plan and counsel women on their short-range job prospects and long term career goals. This may include a period of retraining or up dating at some suitable time in their career, as well as providing a periodic mechanism for feedback on their current performance.

ii. Providing senior management sponsorship. To encourage and help support women managers, a system of sponsorship within the organisation can be useful in the corporate maze. This role would entail helping the female manager meet colleagues, better understand the organisation's informal procedures and customs, and acquaint her with any other peculiarities of corporate life.

iii. Helping male managers to come to terms with women managers. To establish training programmes within the company to get male and female managers to share their perceptions, stereotypes, myths and feelings about one another, and particularly the role of women in management. The goal here is to try and change male managers' views of their female counterpart, and to encourage them to be more supportive and less threatened. The creation of informal support networks for all women managers. This may be particularly helpful while women are still very much in the minority in the organisation, but less necessary as they begin to establish themselves in larger numbers and throughout the organization.

A BUSINESS WOMAN

HOW THE FEMALE MANAGER (OR ANY WOMAN AT WORK) CAN HELP HERSELF COPE WITH STRESS AND BETTER STILL TO AVOID IT

i.   Become aware of being obsessed with time and decide that from now on YOU are in control.

ii. Try to restrain yourself from talking too much, particularly when there is no need to do so. Quietness and silence reflect inner calm constant talking reflects inner turmoil.

iii. Develop reflective periods in your working day to counter 'hurry sickness'.

iv. Tell yourself at least once a day that no enterprise every failed because it was executed carefully and with time but that mistakes always occur when people are rushing.

v.   Indulge in a variety of outside activities, the cinema, hobbies, walking, visiting friends.

vi. Try not to make unnecessary appointments and unachievable deadlines.

vii. Protect your time, learn to say NO.

viii. Take stress free breathing spaces regularly.

ix. Forget about competing with the male sex at work. You have the same brain and nervous system as any man all that separates you from success is not ability but the male culture at work. Simply learn how to function within that culture so that you are taken as seriously as a woman, which means being DIRECT, SAYING WHAT YOU WANT, NOT ACCEPTING COMPROMISES, CONTROLLING EMOTION (WHICH DOES NOT MEAN BEING EMOTIONLESS) BUT SIMPLY LET YOUR HEAD RULE.

x.   ADMIRE YOURSELF AND YOUR ABILITIES - WHY NOT?

VISUALISATION NO.10 - THE COCOON

*You are seated in a quiet and shaded room watching the slowly rotating blades of the
overhead fan casting shadows on the ceiling above.
As you dreamily watch the shadows playing on the plaster above, you feel a sense of
timelessness and you begin to relax.*

*As you relax you feel a sensation of warmth coming up from below enveloping you and
wrapping around you like a blanket as if you were a centre of a cocoon.
This is not an unpleasant sensation but rather one which makes
you feel secure and looked after.*

*As the warmth of the cocoon eases out your everyday
tensions and worries you feel your inner self opening out to absorb the warmth right
inside you and to make it part of your whole being.*

*Let the inner you become one with the warmth coming from below so that it can energise
and reach out into every extremity of your body.
Realise how this warmth is uplifting your mind as well as your body and how by allowing
the warmth inside yourself to mingle with the warmth
from outside, you create a stronger,
less vulnerable and more outgoing bond to life and other people.*

*As you begin to awaken from the dreamlike state you see
the blades of the fan still circling above you and the cocoon dissolves
away leaving you as you were before
but with more positive feeling and confidence than you ever expected to experience.*

VISUALISATION NO.10 - THE COCOON

NOW Read the passage again.

PLAY THE AUDIO